Student Workbook
Level

A Reason For Spelling ® Student Workbook - Level B
Copyright ©1999 by The Concerned Group, Inc.

ISBN#0-936785-27-6

Created by MOE Studio, Inc.

Authors: Rebecca Burton, Eva Hill, Leah Knowlton, Kay Sutherland
Black and White Illustrations: James McCullough
Colorization: Mark Decker, Greg Wolverton
Design and Layout: Greg Hauth • Project Leader: Greg Sutherland

Published by Concerned Communications
Post Office Box 1000, 700 East Granite, Siloam Springs, Arkansas 72761

Publisher: Russ L. Potter, II • Senior Editor: Bill Morelan
Copy Editors: Mary Alice Hill, Edward Sutherland • Story Editor: Tricia Schnell
Support Staff: Jeanne Jensen, Stephanie Schiltz

For more information about *A Reason For Spelling*®,
A Reason For Writing®, or other Concerned Communications curricula,
write to the address above or call:
(501) 549-9000

A | Poetry Connection

Name _____

The Universe God Made

God made a lot of round things
Like the earth and shining stars,
The sun, and moon, and planets:
Venus, Mercury, Saturn, Mars.

He hung them all up in the sky
To show His love and care;
So when I see their shining light
I know that God is there.

Fill in the letter that comes between the given letters.

1. a ___ c   x ___ z   t ___ v

2. j ___ l   k ___ m   n ___ p

3. v ___ x   m ___ o   d ___ f

4. e ___ g   b ___ d   p ___ r

5. g ___ i   s ___ u   h ___ j

6. q ___ s   w ___ y   c ___ e

Write the letter that comes before and after the given letter.

7. __ c __   __ w __   __ s __

8. __ q __   __ e __   __ v __

9. __ h __   __ y __   __ t __

10. __ o __   __ k __   __ m __

3

Name _____

Write the words from each group in ABC order.

1. fire _____

ball _____

apple _____

circle _____

dime _____

earth _____

3. quarter _____

Orion _____

night _____

moon _____

planets _____

round _____

2. heaven _____

Jupiter _____

God _____

light _____

keep _____

ice _____

4. want _____

stars _____

zenith _____

Venus _____

universe _____

telescope _____

Alphabetical Order

Day

1

4

A Poetry Connection

Name _____

Slanted and Straight

The roof of our house slants this way and that,
It sits up on top like a party hat.
The walls of our house are tall and straight.
They're built very strong to hold up the weight.
The floor of our house is level and flat,
So things will stay put—I'm thankful for that!

Say the name of each picture. Write the letter for the beginning sound to complete each name.

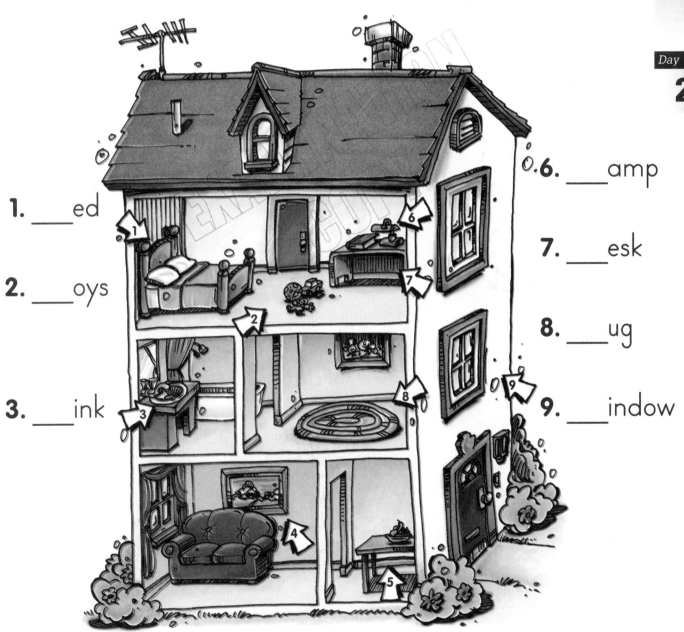

1. ___ed

2. ___oys

3. ___ink

4. ___icture

5. ___able

6. ___amp

7. ___esk

8. ___ug

9. ___indow

Say the name of each picture. Circle the letter that stands for the beginning sound.

1.

2.

3.

r   h   n   m   b   w   d   l   z   s   c   w

4.

5.

6.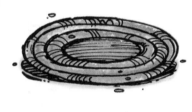

m   p   b   l   b   p   q   k   w   g   r   q

7.

8.

9.

d   p   t   z   f   h   g   n   p   r   m   n

A Poetry Connection

I wonder if...

Long ago and far away
Children gathered 'round to play,
Swung a stick and hit a ball.
Lots of fun for one and all.

But the clay ball broke and cracked
Every time that it got whacked!
So, making changes day by day,
They came up with other ways.

Today, we hear the baseball score,
Golf, softball, and many more.
Perhaps it started (could be true)
With children playing, just like you!

Say the name of each picture. Write the letter for the beginning sound to complete each name.

1.

___all

2.

___ie

3.

___oll

4.

___og

5.

___ame

6.

___oat

B Phonics

Name _____

Say the name of each picture. Write the uppercase and lowercase partner letters for the beginning sound.

1.

_____

2.

_____

3.

_____

4.

_____

5.

_____

6.

_____

7.

_____

8.

_____

9.

_____

A Poetry Connection

Baby Toes

When I was a baby, small as could be,
Mom counted my fingers and toes.
She made up a song, to sing just for me,
And this is the way it goes…

One, two,—three, four, five…
Little bees buzzing out of the hive,
Five, four,—three, two, one…
Better look out, 'cause here they come!

Say the name of each picture. Write the letter for the ending sound to complete each name.

1.

sta___

2.

mitte___

3.

win___

4.

fou___

5.

le___

6.

han___

Name _____

Say the name of each picture. Write the letter for the ending sound.

1.

2.

3.

_____   _____   _____

4.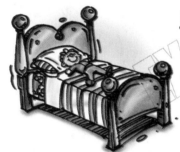

5.

6.

_____   _____   _____

7.

8.

9.

_____   _____   _____

A Poetry Connection

Growing Pains

When I was just six, age seven looked fine.
When seven, I longed to be eight!
And now that I'm eight, I just want to be nine,
For I know being nine would be great.

When I get to ten, I'll almost be grown!
But Dad says when I'm a man,
I'll wish for the day when I was a boy
So be glad for the age that I am!

Say the name of each picture. Find the picture whose name will best complete each sentence. Write the middle letter to complete each name.

1. She had six le___ons for the pie.

2. That ti___er is big!

3. I ate se___en nuts.

4. The ca___el is brown.

5. Pull the red wa___on.

6. Did you see eight legs on the spi___er?

7. We can go to the ca___in.

8. This is my ra___io.

B Phonics

Name _____

Say the name of each picture. Write the letter for the consonant sound you hear in the middle of each word.

1.

_____

2.

_____

3.

_____

4.

_____

5.

_____

6.

_____

7.

_____

8.

_____

9.

_____

A **Poetry Connection**

Name _____

Otters at Play

Alphie and Dan were otter "best friends"
That lived by a lake in the woods
At the top of a mountain that everyone called,
"I'd-Climb-To-The-Top-If-I-Could."

Now, Alphie and Dan always played chase,
And wrestled and tickled and hid.
One day they were rolling and having such fun,
Straight down to the bottom they slid!

They couldn't climb up to get back to their home.
Going that way would take until dawn!
Then, they spotted a limber pine growing near by,
Bent it down, held it fast, and climbed on.

"Here we go," Danny cried, with a lopsided grin,
Alphie laughed, "We'll sure land with a plop!"
And when they let go... well, that tall, taut tree,
Sailed them up and right back to the top!

Say the name of each picture, and write the name on the first line. On the next line, write a word that rhymes with it.

1. _____

2. _____

3. _____

4. _____

5. _____

6. _____

7. _____

8. _____

13

B | Phonics

Circle the word that names each picture.

1.

hot   pot   fox

2.

doll   otter   top

3.

box   log   rock

4.

cob   cot   fox

5.

pot   lot   rob

6.

mob   mop   top

7.

log   just   jog

8.

tip   pot   top

9.

dog   hog   done

Deeds of Kindness

Every act of kindness,
Every word and deed
Plants within someone's heart
A tiny, happy seed.

The seed begins to blossom,
To send down roots and grow.
Soon happiness is passed along
To everyone you know.

Circle the word that best completes each sentence and write it on the line.

1. Jen shared her blue _____.

red   pen   best

2. Ted will ride on the green _____.

sled   bed   desk

3. Mom _____ the hens some corn.

vet   pen   fed

4. We gave the _____ flowers to Grandma.

red   bet   peg

5. The _____ was the right size for Ben.

get   held   tent

6. Tell Tom to _____ Dad.

peck   led   help

7. I sat at a friend's _____.

nest   desk   rest

15

Name _____

Circle the word that names each picture.

1.

hen hand pen

2.

fed met nest

3.

net web bed

4.

peck sled vet

5.

log leg lid

6.

pan pen pond

7.

belt bend bell

8.

bed west web

9.

tent jet peg

A Poetry Connection

Name _____

Lots of Little Things

I always keep my pockets full,
With lots of little things.
Like marbles, pennies, bottle caps,
And little bits of string.

Sometimes when Mama does the wash,
And dumps my pockets out,
I race into the laundry room
Because I hear her shout!

And there stands Mom, white as a sheet,
And trying not to cry.
Because she's found a small thing in
My pocket that's ALIVE!

Color the oval in front of the sentence that tells about each picture. Draw circles around all /i/ words in the sentences.

1. ○ Bill bit his lip.
   ○ Bill will run up the hill.
   ○ Bill has an ink pen.
   ○ Bill drinks a lot of milk.

2. ○ Sid did spill the pins.
   ○ Sid will lift the lid.
   ○ Sid will eat the chips and dip.
   ○ Sid can fill the dish with dill.

3. ○ The king has a big pig.
   ○ The king put a dish in the sink.
   ○ The king hid in the big box.
   ○ The king sat on the big fish.

The Sound of /i/

Day 8

17

Name _____

Write the word that names each picture by filling in the missing letters.

The Sound of /i/

1.

__ i __

2.

__ i __

3.

__ i __ __ __

4.

__ i __ __

5.

__ i __

6.

__ i __

7.

__ i __ __

8.

__ i __

9.

__ i __ __

Name _____

Truly Conceivable

Some say it's unbelievable,
And truly inconceivable,
Our Father made the birds that sing,
Long, long ago the stars did fling.

Some say it's unbelievable,
And truly inconceivable,
Our Father loves the world so much,
He sent His Son to die for us.

Some say it's unbelievable,
And truly inconceivable,
That Jesus wants to guide our way,
And care for us from day to day.

To me it's so believable,
And easily conceivable.
It's not because I'm really smart.
I know—because He's in my heart!

Say the name of each picture. Circle the picture if the word has the sound of **/u/** in the middle.

1.

2.

3.

4.

5.

6.

Circle the word that best completes each sentence and write it on the line.

1. I had a _____ of milk.

    cup   bag

2. He saw a black _____ on the wall.

    bus   bug

3. Russ can _____ and run.

    net   jump

4. The dog sat on the _____.

    rug   run

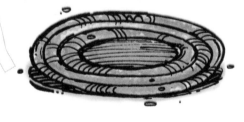

5. Did she _____ her leg?

    cut   as

6. That white duck cannot _____ fast.

    cap   run

7. I like red _____ the best.

    six   gum

8. Was it _____ to ride the bike?

    fun   kit

9. We sat in the hot _____.

    big   sun

10. I gave my mom a big _____.

    hug   hill

Name _____

Bubble Gum

I really do love chewing gum.
Blowing bubbles is lots of fun.
I chew gum quiet, chew it loud,
I chew alone, or in a crowd.

I chew it fast, I chew it slow,
But either way, one thing I know:
That when the flavor's gone at last,
I'll throw my gum into the trash.

For I know gum is fun to chew,
But not to find upon your shoe!
'Cause in my mouth it's soft and chewy,
But on the sidewalk, gross and gooey.

And so this promise I have made,
And with this promise I have stayed:
My chewing gum will not be found
Upon the sidewalk, street, or ground!

Say the name of each picture. Circle the picture if the word has the sound of **/g/**.

1.

2.

3.

4.

5.

6.

Name _____

Say each word. If it has the sound of **/j/**, write it in the top column. If the word has the sound of **/g/**, write it in the bottom column.

Soft g   /j/

1. _____
2. _____
3. _____
4. _____
5. _____
6. _____
7. _____

Hard g   /g/

8. _____
9. _____
10. _____
11. _____
12. _____
13. _____
14. _____

Word Bank

age	gave	giant	goes	goose	stage	wagon
cage	gem	God	good	gym	tag	wage

22

A Poetry Connection

Mice in the Night

One night my mom went down the stairs,
And in the kitchen saw a pair
Of mice behind the plastic bin
She keeps the new potatoes in.

My mother gave a dreadful wail,
Then grabbed a bag and let it sail.
It flew—then landed with such fury
That the mice began to scurry.

Then Dad ran into the kitchen,
He lost his balance, and started slippin'
Because the floor was slick as ice—
My mom had thrown a bag of rice!

So now Dad has a broken arm,
Because of the "night mice" alarm.
If Mom ever sees more mice,
She'll grab a broom instead of rice!

Say the name of each picture. Circle the picture if the word has the sound of /k/.

1.

2.

3.

4.

5.

6.

Circle the word that best completes each sentence and write it on the line.

1. The dog was _____ to me.

    nice   face

2. Mike put the _____ in the bag.

    can   race

3. Mom made a _____ cap for my doll.

    mice   lace

4. I like _____ with milk.

    cement   rice

5. You can bake a _____ for Dad.

    cake   fence

6. This red _____ is too big for me.

    celery   coat

7. Joe and Tom will run the _____.

    race   rice

8. Please light the _____ on the cake.

    candies   candles

9. Dad said not to climb the _____.

    fence   fact

10. We went to see the _____.

    circus   circles

Name _____

Compound Words

I've discovered, just like you,
That one plus one adds up to two.
But just today, I thought of this
And realized a point I'd missed!

I had some oatmeal, creamy hot.
I sprinkled sugar on the top.
I watched that sugar melt right in.
I stirred it up, and thought with a grin...

There are some times when two together
Add up to just one—one thing that's better!

Choose the two words that go together to make a new word. You can make four new words from each set. Write the four new words on the lines.

tea	coat	**1.** _____
sail	pot	**2.** _____
mail	boat	**3.** _____
rain	box	**4.** _____
bath	boy	**5.** _____
cow	road	**6.** _____
rail	be	**7.** _____
may	tub	**8.** _____
base	mate	**9.** _____
class	self	**10.** _____
day	ball	**11.** _____
my	dream	**12.** _____

Name _____

Put each set of words together to make a new word. **Write** the word on the line, then read the sentence.

1. oat+meal   I like _____ with brown sugar.

2. pan+cake   Mom puts butter on each _____.

3. cup+cake   May I have a _____?

4. sea+weed   There is _____ on the sand.

5. base+ball   Will you play _____ next spring?

6. pea+nut   We gave a _____ to the monkey.

7. rain+coat   Did you wear a _____?

8. dog+house   We helped Dad build a _____.

9. blue+berry   Is this _____ ripe?

10. mail+box   Take this letter to the _____.

11. foot+ball   We like to play _____.

12. bath+tub   Mom made me wash in the _____.

A Poetry Connection

Name _____

Right or Wrong

Right or wrong, right or wrong.
Sometimes its hard to know
Whether something's right or wrong,
Or which way we should go.

But when we make bad choices
And ask God to forgive,
He loves to take away our sin
And show us how to live.

Name one of God's gifts to answer these riddles. Each answer is a word with a final cluster.

1. I am an animal God made.
You do not like to have me around.
I am a _____.

2. Cows eat grass to make this.
I am something to drink.
I am _____.

3. Turtles and frogs live near me.
I am a good home for fish.
I am a _____.

4. Birds build this in a tree.
I am a home for their babies.
I am a _____.

Word Bank

milk   nest   pond   skunk

Name _____

Say the name of each picture. Write the final cluster to complete each word.

1.

ri ___ ___

2.

sta ___ ___

3.

te ___ ___

4.

sku ___ ___

5.

mi ___ ___

6.

ra ___ ___

7.

ne ___ ___

8.

li ___ ___

9.

ce ___ ___

A Poetry Connection

Name _____

Rainy Day

This morning's weather? We have rain!
I'm staring out the window pane
And wondering what to do.

I guess that I could bake a cake,
Or make a purple play dough snake,
Or read a book or two.

I guess I could watch for the mail,
Or make a paper boat to sail,
Or build with sticks and glue.

But maybe, maybe if I wait,
The rain will start to dissipate,
And the sun will shine right through.

Then if Mother says, "Okay,"
I'll run right outside and play
And find a friend or two.

Find the word that best completes each sentence and write it on the line.

1. Kate _____ a cake for Mom.

2. Steve can hike to the _____.

3. Dave put the _____ in the box.

4. We cannot _____ up late.

5. _____ the leaves into a pile.

6. Kay _____ the man for the grapes.

7. Put these roses in a _____.

8. What is his _____?

Word Bank

cave	mail	paid	stay
made	name	rake	vase

The Sound of /ā/

Day
14

29

Write the word that names each picture by filling in the missing vowels.

1.

f ___ ___ t

2.

j ___ ___ p

3.

g ___ m ___

4.

t ___ ___ th

5.

tr ___ ___

6.

r ___ ___ n

7.

c ___ k ___

8.

s ___ ___ l

9.

sn ___ k ___

Word Bank

cake	game	rain	snake	tree
feet	jeep	sail	teeth	

A Poetry Connection

My Perfect Day
The clouds are white and fluffy,
There's blue sky, there's sunshine,
The autumn leaves are colored bright,
The soft breeze feels just fine.

The pretty flowers are blooming,
Grapes ripen on the vine.
This day is simply perfect, Lord.
Thank you that it's mine.

Read each riddle and circle the correct answer.

1. It is something that blows gently. What is it?

bread   breeze

2. It can jump and hop. What is it?

frog   free

3. We sometimes eat it for a snack. What is it?

grass   fruit

4. This grows in our yard. What is it?

train   tree

5. It is something good to eat. What is it?

grapes   grade

6. It is something fun to play with. What is it?

trail   train

B **Phonics**

Name _____

Circle the word that names each picture.

1.  **2.**  **3.**

grapes   grades   trust   truck   from   frog

4.  **5.**  **6.**

drive   drum   tree   trim   train   trade

Find the **r** cluster in each word and write the letters on the line.

1. grapes   **2.** truck   **3.** train

_____   _____   _____

4. drink   **5.** drum   **6.** dress

_____   _____   _____

7. brick   **8.** branch   **9.** crowd

_____   _____   _____

A **Poetry Connection**   Name _____

Faith in God

I look up to the heavens
And think of God above.
I thank Him for His goodness,
His patience and His love.

I know that I can trust Him.
My faith in Him is strong.
And soon He'll come again to take me
Home where I belong.

Read the sentence and circle the correct answer on the right. Circle the word or words in each sentence that have the sound of **/ü/** or **/ū/**.

Is It True?

1. She can play a tune on a flute.   Yes   No

2. The red shirt is blue.   Yes   No

3. An ice cube is cold.   Yes   No

4. A kitten is cute.   Yes   No

5. Luke wrote part of the Bible.   Yes   No

6. A mule eats at the table.   Yes   No

7. I use a fork to write with.   Yes   No

8. He can float on a tube.   Yes   No

9. June is a day of the week.   Yes   No

10. It is rude to hit others.   Yes   No

Circle the words from the Word Bank in the puzzle.

r	u	L	e	b	c	f	t	u	b	e	f
u	c	u	b	e	g	i	k	m	l	o	q
d	a	k	e	s	r	t	v	J	u	n	e
e	x	e	z	a	c	c	u	t	e	e	g
h	m	j	l	m	o	p	s	r	t	u	w
t	u	n	e	b	d	f	e	a	r	v	y
f	l	u	t	e	u	j	u	y	h	i	f
e	e	s	b	o	r	m	u	c	t	h	a

Word Bank

blue	cute	June	mule	rule	tune
cube	flute	Luke	rudle	tube	use

Name _____

Jesus is Kind

Some mothers brought their children for Jesus to bless,
But his helpers said, "No! He does not need more stress."
The children turned sadly and started to go,
When Jesus said, "Come, I love children so!"
He kindly talked with them all through the day.
They were so glad He'd allowed them to stay.

Circle the word that best completes each sentence and write it on the line.

1. Mark will hit the ball _____.

    high   hen   hill

2. She can ride her _____ today.

    bike   bill   big

3. I _____ to jump over the creek.

    lick   life   like

4. We made a _____ to get warm.

    five   fine   fire

5. There are a lot of bees in that _____.

    hit   hive   hip

6. Can you tell _____?

    tire   time   tick

7. The _____ under our sink broke.

    pipe   pit   pie

8. Jimmy has a big blue _____.

    kit   kite   kick

Circle the word that best completes each sentence.

The Sound of /ō/

1. Will you jump (rope, rod) with me?

2. My dad needs to (mop, mow) the grass.

3. That (got, goat) is eating a shirt!

4. Mom wrote a (not, note) to my teacher.

5. Hang your (coat, cot) up on the hook.

6. There is a big (hop, hole) in this bag.

7. Tony (rock, rode) home with us.

8. My (not, nose) was cold and red.

9. Did you (fog, fold) the clothes?

10. The green (toad, top) croaked loudly.

11. The boys can (row, romp) the boat.

12. Ask (Joan, jam) to bring a robe.

A Poetry Connection

Name _____

Baby Bird

Follow me quick, but hush, now, hush.
There's something new in the blackberry bush.

A skinny thing, no feathers or fur.
It's cheeping and peeping, and causing a stir!

It wants food fast—but hush, don't speak.
Here comes Mama with a cricket in her beak.

Circle the word that best completes each sentence and write it on the line.

Day
18

1. The vase has a _____ at the top.

    crack   black

2. I like to _____ in the tub.

    splash   dash

3. Did you _____ your teeth?

    shine   brush

4. A big _____ is at the dock.

    lock   ship

5. His dog did a _____.

    trick   quack

6. The pink _____ is on the sand.

    shell   snack

7. He has black _____ on his feet.

    sacks   shoes

8. I will clean the blue _____ with a cloth.

    stack   dish

B **Phonics**

Name _____

Say the name of each picture. Circle the letters that stand for the consonant digraph in each name.

1.

ck   sh

2.

sh   ck

3.

sh   ck

4.

sh   ck

5.

sh   ck

6.

sh   ck

7.

sh   ck

8.

sh   ck

9.

sh   ck

A **Poetry Connection**

Name _____

The Little Things

The puzzling thing about puzzles,
Is all the pieces, you see.
When I first look at a pile of them,
They all look alike to me!
But I really try hard, and am happy to say,
That before I know it, I'm done.
Then feeling quite pleased, I think to myself,
"Now, I'll try a bigger one!"

Read each word. If the **y** has an /ē/ sound, color that puzzle piece blue.

1. try
2. windy
3. happy
4. my
5. puppy
6. rocky

Underline each word in which **y** has an /ī/ sound.

Tommy can fry an egg in this pan.

A plane can fly high in the sky.

There is a bunny by that tree.

Why did he cry when he saw the puppy?

39

B **Phonics**

Name _____

Circle the word in each set in which **y** has the sound of /ē/.

1. shiny   **2.** my   **3.** penny   **4.** tiny

fly   dry   try   fry

why   funny   shy   cry

Choose the word from the Word Bank below that best completes each sentence. Then write it on the line.

1. Please _____ to talk softly.

2. Put the ball _____ my books.

3. I have a dime to buy a piece of _____.

4. Billy can make _____ faces.

5. It is too _____ to fly my kite.

6. _____ are you crying?

Word Bank

by   candy   funny   try   why   windy

A Poetry Connection

Name _____

Hello, Mr. Wind

I love to hear the wild, wild wind
Whipping and whistling through
The open windows, under doors
And up the chimney flue.

And though I know it's just the wind
Doing what wind should do
Sometimes it's funny to pretend
It's someone I once knew.

So out I run to our front yard
And wave my arms and yell,
"Hello there, friend! You going far?
You're rushing, I can tell!"

And as the leaves descend and swirl,
I pretend I hear him say,
"Just passin' through to say hello,
Can't stop to chat today!"

Read each riddle. Choose the correct answer and write it on the line.

1. I am a tool. A plumber uses me.
What am I? _____

2. I live in the ocean. I am very big.
What am I? _____

3. I grow in a field. I am used to make bread.
What am I? _____

4. I am part of a wagon. I am round.
What am I? _____

Word Bank

wheat   wheel   wrench   whale

Consonant Digraphs wh, wr

Day

20

Circle the word that best completes each sentence and write it on the line.

1. _____ out the wet towel.

     Wring   What

2. Brad fell and broke his _____.

     wheat   wrist

3. Grandpa _____ me a letter.

     wreck   wrote

4. _____ are you going?

     Wren   Where

5. It is _____ to tell a lie.

     wrong   whale

6. There are _____ in her dress.

     wrinkles   write

7. Can you _____ this gift?

     wheel   wrap

8. Did you eat the _____ piece of cake?

     wrench   whole

9. We saw a _____ on the "Ocean" video.

     wheat   whale

10. Dad is going to paint the house _____.

     where   white

Six Little Eggs
Six little eggs in a mockingbird's nest.
Mother bird is warming them while she rests.
Father bird is singing loudly all the songs he's heard.
And guess who soon will sing with him?
Six more little birds!

Circle the word that best completes each sentence.

1. Timmy is outside _____ the dog.

   feed   feeding   feeds

2. Mr. Brown _____ on the fence all day.

   working   works   worked

3. Will you _____ to the store with me?

   walked   walk   walks

4. I like _____ down the creek in a tube.

   floated   float   floating

5. Our family went _____ at the lake.

   fishes   fishing   fished

6. Are you _____ for your mom?

   look   looked   looking

7. The frogs _____ into the pond.

   jump   jumping   jumped

8. Danny is _____ Allen with his math.

   helping   helped   helps

Find the word that best completes each sentence and write it on the line.

Suffix -ing

Day

21

1. We will be _____ hot dogs at six.

2. Shelly is _____ on one leg.

3. Bring your _____ bag with you.

4. Which team is _____ the game?

5. Adam is going _____ at the pool.

6. They are _____ candles to sell.

7. Mom took my sister _____ for shoes.

8. Dad is _____ at a new job today.

9. The policeman is _____ the cars.

10. I should buy a tent for our _____ trip.

11. The children are _____ for the bus.

12. Erin is _____ the kitten.

Word Bank

camping	hopping	roasting	sleeping	swimming	winning
dipping	petting	shopping	stopping	waiting	working

Name _____

Hide and Seek

Our little brother likes to play
The game of hide and seek,
But every time that he is "It"
He always wants to peek.

So we explain, "You mustn't look,
Or you'll see where we run."
And every time, he nods his head
And starts again at "one."

So off we go to find a spot—
That perfect hiding place,
But sure enough, we turn around
To see that chubby face.

He'll laugh and squeal with sheer delight
And grab us by the legs,
And though he just now caught us both,
"Play more!" he'll start to beg.

We roll our eyes and shake our heads,
And say the rules again.
But I think it would really help
If he could count to ten!

Say the name of each picture. Write the cluster that stands for the sound you hear at the beginning of each word.

1.  ____

3.  ____

5.  ____

2.  ____

4.  ____

6.  ____

Answer Bank

bl	cl	dr	fl	pl	st

Find the word that best completes each sentence and write it on the line.

1. Dad can _____ stones on the lake.

2. We will _____ for the funny clown.

3. Put the cheese on that _____.

4. The dish is made of _____.

5. I like to pick _____.

6. Mike did not _____ the milk.

7. Did you _____ the can of peas?

8. The cake _____ very good.

9. Mr. Hanson drives a red _____.

10. A _____ is a black bird.

11. Mom wants us to use the rake on the _____.

12. My _____ are too small this winter.

Word Bank

clap	drink	glass	grass	skip	spill
crow	flowers	gloves	plate	smells	truck

A Poetry Connection

Name _____

Character

School is fun, a happy place,
I'm learning lots of stuff!
But Mama says that learning math
And spelling's not enough.

Our teachers here want us to know
How children should behave.
So, when we first arrived at school,
These are the rules they gave:

"When walking down the hall, you must
March straight in single file.
And hang your coats upon the hooks,
Don't drop them in a pile."

"When time for lunch, your forks and spoons,
You really must not rattle.
Be kind to all. Please understand,
It's very rude to tattle."

My mama says that this is good,
That "character" will grow.
And though I don't know what that means,
When I have it, it will show!

Find the word that best completes each sentence and write it on the line.

1. It is fun to _____ my sister.

2. Worms _____ in the mud after it rains.

3. The _____ of the pot is hot.

4. Dad put the _____ on the horse.

5. An _____ is a huge bird.

6. Do you like to eat _____?

Word Bank

eagle   handle   pickles   saddle   tickle   wiggle

B Phonics

Name _____

Find the word that names each picture and write it on the line.

1.

2.

3.

_____ _____

4.

5.

6.

_____ _____ _____

7.

8.

9.

_____ _____ _____

Word Bank

apple	buckle	circle	rattle	thimble
bubbles	candle	people	table	

A Poetry Connection

Name _____

I've Been Everywhere

I've been to lots of places in the years I've been alive.
And I've seen a million faces, 'cause my daddy likes to drive!

I've seen Ohio's rivers, and Missouri's famous zoo.
I've been in Pennsylvania, covered most of Boston, too!

We stopped in Houston, Texas, spent a day in Delaware.
Saw chickens in Rhode Island, toured the Kansas City Fair.

Stood 'neath California's redwoods, drove across Dakota's hills,
Stared amazed at Niagara Falls, and Wisconsin's mighty mills.

Touched the Great Salt Lake in Utah, then to Georgia made a trek.
Took my Grandpa to Lake Erie, after jaunting through Quebec.

When I say, "We've been everywhere!" Dad spins the globe with glee.
He spreads his arms wide, and declares, "There's a whole world yet to see!"

Circle the word that best completes each sentence.

1. Her (cheeks, peach) are red from the cold.

2. (Chin, Cheer) for your favorite baseball team.

3. Dave sat in the blue (chew, chair).

4. (The, They) went to the park to play.

5. Please hand me (that, those) blocks.

6. (Chop, Cheese) wood for the fire, please.

7. Do you (think, thing) we can go?

8. I need to give my dog a (thank, bath).

Consonant Digraphs th, ch

Day
24

49

Name _____

Say each word. If the consonant digraph is at the beginning of the word, write it in the first column. If it is in the middle, write it in the second column. If it is at the end, write it in the third column.

Beginning	Middle	End
1. _____	6. _____	11. _____
2. _____	7. _____	12. _____
3. _____	8. _____	13. _____
4. _____	9. _____	14. _____
5. _____	10. _____	

Word Bank

beaches	cheek	chips	coaching	peach	teacher	think
bench	chin	clothing	neither	reach	teeth	this

A Poetry Connection

Name _____

Jesus Loves Me

Jesus loves me! How do I know?
Things He created tell me so.
The pretty flowers in colors bright,
The moon and stars that shine at night,
The seasons as they come and go,
The rain and sun to help food grow,
God's Word with stories of long ago
All tell of Jesus' love, I know.

Color in the oval in front of the sentence that tells about each picture. Draw a circle around each word that begins with the digraph **kn**.

1. ○ Jeff does not know the answer.
   ○ Jeff turned the door knob.
   ○ Jeff has a knot in his shoe lace.

2. ○ Nancy knelt down by her bed.
   ○ Nancy knocked on the door.
   ○ Nancy can knit a scarf.

3. ○ Dad put a new knob on the door.
   ○ Dad hit his knee on the chair.
   ○ Dad cut the bread with a knife.

Think of a word that starts with **kn** and rhymes with each word. Write it on the line.

1. snow _____   **4.** wife _____

2. hot _____   **5.** cob _____

3. see _____

B **Phonics**   Name _____

Circle the word that best completes each sentence.

1. Look at those shiny _____.

   star   stars

2. We have many _____ in our yard.

   flower   flowers

3. The _____ is very heavy.

   box   boxes

4. We ate the bunch of _____.

   grape   grapes

5. There are four _____ in a year.

   season   seasons

Say each word. If the word means one, write it in the left column. If the word means more than one, write it in the right column.

One

1. _____
2. _____
3. _____
4. _____
5. _____

More than One

6. _____
7. _____
8. _____
9. _____
10. _____

Word Bank

| apple | bowl | dishes | kitten | pencils |
| bananas | color | glasses | peaches | sandwich |

A Poetry Connection

Matthew and Mark

I open my Bible, it's God's Holy Word.
I turn through the pages to stories I've heard.
I'm glad God had men write these stories so true,
So they'd be recorded for me and for you.

Matthew wrote about Jesus' birth,
His life and ministry while on earth.
Matthew proved Jesus is the Messiah
Who fulfilled the prophecies of Isaiah.

Mark wrote of Jesus' ministry,
His life and teachings in Galilee.
Mark emphasized what Jesus did
More than just what Jesus said.

Circle the word that names the picture.

1.

can corn cone

2.

for fort fork

3.

star stop stir

4.

doll dart damp

5.

barn back bark

6.

have horse hope

Name _____

Read each riddle. To find the answer, think of a word that rhymes with the word at the end of each riddle. Write the answer on the line.

1. Pickles come in this.

far _____

2. You push this in a grocery store.

mart _____

3. A vegetable that grows on a stalk.

born _____

4. The opposite of light.

bark _____

5. Part of a car that makes a loud noise.

torn _____

6. It shines in the sky at night.

bar _____

7. A farmer keeps hay and tools in this.

yarn _____

8. A place to shop.

more _____

9. Something sharp on the stem of a rose.

worn _____

A **Poetry Connection**

Name _____

Luke and John

I open my Bible, it's God's Holy Word.
I turn through the pages to stories I've heard.
I'm glad God had men write these stories so true,
So they'd be recorded for me and for you.

Doctor Luke wrote his gospel in such a fine style
Everyone understood it, both Jew and Gentile.
He wrote about Jesus from birth to ascension,
So we'd understand God's great salvation.

John speaks of Jesus in tones of such love
That we look to the Father in Heaven above.
John tells us Jesus, who some called the Christ,
Brings truth, and salvation, and eternal life.

Circle the word that best completes each sentence.

1. Luke wrote about the _____ of Jesus.

earth   birth   burn

2. I _____ the pages in my Bible carefully.

verse   earn   turn

3. Jesus died so we can have _____ life.

eternal   evening   earnest

4. It makes me happy to go to _____.

crumb   church   curb

5. The _____ sang all morning.

worms   birds   chirp

6. The little _____ is eating an acorn.

squirrel   squash   short

Name _____

Circle each word with the same sound as the name of the picture.

1.	2.	3.

bird / ir	hurt / ur	herd / er
first	fur	germ
shirt	turtle	stern
horse	church	short
girl	start	merge
thirty	purse	person

Find the name of each picture in the lists above. Write the names on the lines.

1.	2.	3.

_____	_____	_____

A Poetry Connection

Name _____

Fruits of the Spirit

Love helps a boy and girl put their toys away,
Joy helps a boy and girl be cheerful everyday.
Peace helps a boy and girl be happy, never mad,
God's Spirit lives within our hearts
And makes us glad, glad, glad.

Circle the word that names each picture.

1.

tails   toys   tows

2.

nose   notes   noise

3.

point   paint   pint

4.

boy   boil   bone

5.

coins   cons   cones

6.

say   sail   soil

7.

boy   done   bone

8.

all   oil   ail

9.

coin   cony   coil

B Phonics

Name _____

Read each sentence. Find the word in the word bank that best completes each sentence. Write it on the line.

1. The _____ won the race.

2. Some people collect stamps or _____.

3. The horn makes a loud _____.

4. _____ splatters are hard to clean.

5. A fruit of the spirit is _____.

6. He put _____ in the flower pot.

7. Sam got more _____ for his birthday.

8. The _____ on my pencil broke.

9. The water began to _____.

10. Would you like to _____ God's family?

Word Bank

boil	coins	joy	oil	soil
boy	join	noise	point	toys

Name _____

House on the Rock

If you hear the words of Jesus
But His voice you don't obey
Then you are like that foolish man
Who lost his house one day.

He had built upon the soft sand,
His foundations weren't dug deep.
When rain came down, and rivers flowed,
His house fell in a heap.

So please, put into practice
All the words you hear God say.
He is the Rock, so you'll be strong.
Sin can't wash you away.

Read each riddle. Choose the correct answer and write it on the line.

1. I come in many colors.

I grow in the yard. What am I? _____

2. I am a direction.

Birds fly this way in winter. What am I? _____

3. I hunt at night.

I live in a tree. What am I? _____

4. I am something to wear.

You will wear one in heaven. What am I? _____

5. A farmer uses me.

I dig up the ground. What am I? _____

Word Bank

crown   flowers   owl   plow   south

Read each sentence. Find the word in the word bank that best completes each sentence.
Write it on the line.

1. There are pretty _____ in her yard.

2. A house built on sand will fall _____.

3. You must build your _____ on solid rock.

4. Jesus has promised us a _____ in heaven.

5. An _____ hooted near our tent.

6. Jesus will come in a _____ of angels.

7. Mother said I must go home _____.

8. The squirrel has _____ fur.

9. We went to _____ to do some shopping.

10. I learned _____ to plant a garden.

Word Bank

brown	crown	flowers	how	owl
cloud	down	house	now	town

A Poetry Connection

Name _____

Contradictions

The Pharisees and Scribes, who were teachers of the law,
Watched Jesus very closely, never liking what they saw.
They'd made a lot of extra rules for people to obey,
But Jesus showed the growing crowds that this was not His way.
God's laws were most important, and not these rules of men.
Our Father loves and heals us, and He saves us from our sin.

Write the sentences in the correct order on the lines. Use a contraction in place of the underlined words. Remember to capitalize and punctuate correctly.

1. like Jesus.   The Pharisees   <u>did not</u>

_____

2. obey God's laws.   <u>I will</u>

_____

3. happy   help others.   <u>We are</u>   when we

_____

4. <u>is not</u>   My house   built on sand.

_____

Word Bank

didn't   I'll   isn't   we're

61

Write the contraction that means the same as the words given.

Contractions: did not = didn't

1. did not _____

5. will not _____

2. cannot _____

6. is not _____

3. could not _____

7. are not _____

4. do not _____

8. were not _____

Write the word or words that mean the same as the underlined contraction.

1. Jesus <u>didn't</u> worry about the Pharisees. _____

2. I <u>won't</u> tell the secret. _____

3. Zacchaeus <u>couldn't</u> see over the crowd. _____

4. Peter <u>isn't</u> catching any fish. _____

5. Why <u>weren't</u> you doing what Mom said? _____

6. The Pharisees <u>don't</u> want Jesus to heal on the Sabbath. _____

7. They <u>aren't</u> coming with us? _____

8. I <u>can't</u> wait until Jesus comes again. _____

Word Bank

aren't	couldn't	don't	weren't
can't	didn't	isn't	won't

Contractions

Day

30

A **Poetry Connection**

Name _____

Sharing With Jesus

The people loved Jesus, and Jesus loved them.
Wherever he went, crowds were following Him.
One day He was preaching and healing the sick,
The people kept coming, the crowd soon grew thick.
The disciples told Jesus, "The people can't stay,
We've nothing to feed them, they must go away."
But Jesus just asked them to wait for a while.
"My God will provide," Jesus said with a smile.
"We do have some fishes and some barley bread,
Brought here by a small lad," the good Andrew said.
And so Jesus took it, He blessed it, and then
It grew to enough to feed five thousand men!
Enough for their families, for everyone there!
Because of a young boy, so willing to share.

Read each sentence. Write the correct suffix **-ed** or **-ing** on each line.

1. A boy want____ to hear Jesus' stories.

2. His mother is pack____ him a lunch.

3. The people were listen____ to Jesus.

4. Jesus ask____ if anyone had food.

5. The people were seat____ on the grass.

6. Jesus asked a bless____ on the food.

7. The disciples pass____ out the food.

8. Jesus began break____ the bread.

B Phonics   Name _____

Read each riddle. Circle the base word in each underlined word. Answer each riddle, using words from the word bank.

Base Words: reading   melted

1. I want to go listen to Jesus.
My mother is packing me a lunch.
Who am I? _____

2. We were placed in a basket with some bread.
There were two of us.
What were we? _____

3. We told the people to be seated.
We were Jesus' special friends.
Who were we? _____

4. I found a small boy with a lunch.
I like talking to people.
Who am I? _____

5. I was put in a basket.
Jesus blessed and broke me.
What was I? _____

Word Bank

Andrew   bread   disciples   fish   small boy

Suffixes -ed, -ing

Day 31

64

A Reason For Spelling®

Dear Parent,

We are about to begin our first spelling unit containing five weekly lessons. A set of ten words plus three challenge words will be studied each week. All the words will be reviewed in the sixth week.

Values based on the Scriptures listed below will be taught in each lesson.

Lesson 1	Lesson 2	Lesson 3	Lesson 4	Lesson 5
add	best	been	box	above
ask	ever	begin	dot	does
camp	head	digit	drop	done
fast	help	give	frog	jump
hat	left	into	gone	just
have	leg	its	lost	must
last	men	kid	lot	none
map	nest	live	odd	number
plan	next	quit	often	sum
than	set	sister	soft	what
☆ apple	☆ again	☆ because	☆ forgot	☆ bubble
☆ asked	☆ never	☆ gym	☆ job	☆ once
☆ bath	☆ sentence	☆ until	☆ tomorrow	☆ sometimes
Matt. 22:37	Luke 9:48	Matt. 5:25	Mark 9:50	Matt. 24:42

A Preview

Write each word as your teacher says it.

Name _____

1. _____

2. _____

3. _____

4. _____

5. _____

6. _____

7. _____

8. _____

9. _____

10. _____

Mrs. Morgan's Class for Center City!

Challenge Words

☆ _____

☆ _____

☆ _____

Scripture

"Love the Lord your God with all your heart, soul, and mind."
Matthew 22:37

Write each word in the correct word shape boxes. Then, in the word shape boxes, color the letter that spells the sound of /a/ in each word. Circle the words that begin with the sound of /a/.

1. add

2. ask

3. camp

4. fast

5. hat

6. have

7. last

8. map

9. plan

10. than

⭐ **Challenge**

Draw the correctly shaped boxes around each letter in these words.

apple   asked   bath

C Hide and Seek

Circle a cookie for each word you spell correctly.

D Other Word Forms

Using the words below, follow the instructions given by your teacher.

adds	camped	lasted
added	camping	lasting
adding	faster	maps
apples	fastest	mapped
asks	has	mapping
asking	had	plans
baths	hats	planned
camps	lasts	planning

E Fun Ways to Spell

Initial the box of each activity you finish.

1.

Spell your words with crayon…

3.

Spell your words with rhythm instruments…

2.

Spell your words with sidewalk chalk…

4.

Spell your words with cotton balls...

Name _____

Write each pair of spelling words in alphabetical order.

1. add   hat   _____ _____
2. plan   camp   _____ _____
3. map   fast   _____ _____
4. than   ask   _____ _____
5. have   last   _____ _____
☆ bath   apple   _____ _____

A B C D E F G H I J K L M N O P Q R S T U V W X Y Z

a b c d e f g h i j k l m n o p q r s t u v w x y z

G Dictation

Name _____

Listen and write the missing words.

1. Tommy _____ _____ _____ _____ _____ .

2. _____ _____ _____ show ___

   ____ way.

3. Mrs. Morgan _____ _____ _____ _____

   _____ _____ .

4. ___ like ___ hike better _____ _____ .

H Proofreading

One word in each set is misspelled. Fill in the oval by the misspelled word.

1. ◯ map
   ◯ asc
   ◯ hat

2. ◯ hav
   ◯ plan
   ◯ than

3. ◯ add
   ◯ kamp
   ◯ last

4. ◯ fatst
   ◯ ask
   ◯ have

5. ◯ than
   ◯ map
   ◯ plon

6. ◯ lasd
   ◯ camp
   ◯ hat

⭐ ◯ appel
   ◯ fast
   ◯ add

⭐ ◯ plan
   ◯ asket
   ◯ add

⭐ ◯ dath
   ◯ last
   ◯ have

I | Game

Name _____

Follow **Tommy** to the pantry to sleep till the tornado is past. **Move** one space for each word you or your team spells correctly from this week's word list.

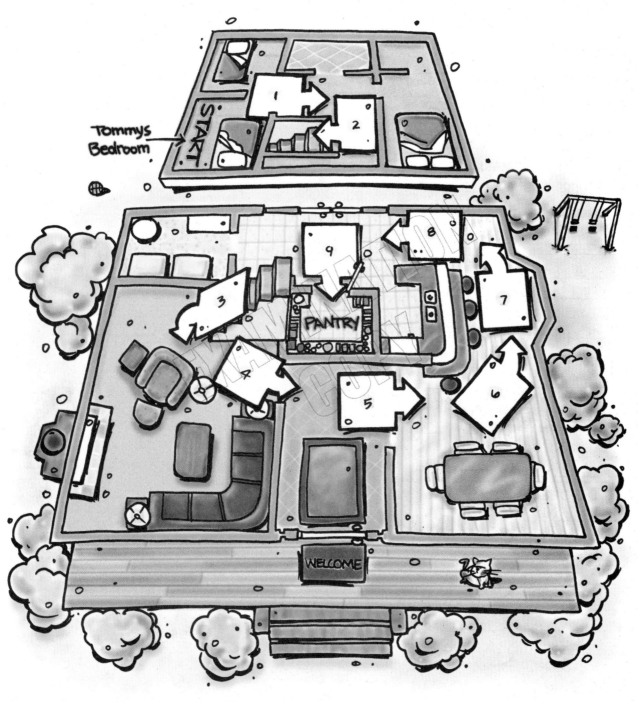

Remember: Choosing to be like Jesus shows that you love Him.

J | Journaling

Copy this sentence in your journal and finish it: **I can show I love God with all my heart, soul, and mind by. . .**

A Preview

Write each word as your teacher says it.

Name _____

1. _____

2. _____

3. _____

4. _____

5. _____

6. _____

7. _____

8. _____

9. _____

10. _____

Words with /e/

Lesson

2

Challenge Words

⭐ _____

⭐ _____

⭐ _____

Scripture

"Your care for others is the measure of your greatness." Luke 9:48

B **Word Shapes**

Name _____

Write each word in the correct word shape boxes. Then, in the word shape boxes, color the letter or letters that spell the sound of /e/ in each word. Circle the word in which the sound of /e/ is spelled with two vowels.

1. best

2. ever

3. head

4. help

5. left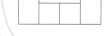

6. leg

7. men

8. nest

9. next

10. set

☆ **Challenge**

Draw the correctly shaped boxes around each letter in these words.

again   never   sentence

C Hide and Seek

Name _____

Circle a cookie for each word you spell correctly.

D Other Word Forms

Using the words below, follow the instructions given by your teacher.

every	legs
heads	man
headed	nests
heading	nesting
helps	sentences
helped	sets
helping	setting
helper	reset

E Fun Ways to Spell

Initial the box of each activity you finish.

1. ☐

Spell your words with an eraser…

3. ☐

Spell your words with clapping…

2. ☐

Spell your words with paint...

4. ☐

Spell your words in wet sand…

Name _____

Change the underlined letter or letters and write the spelling word on the blank.

1. _____ Is there a baby bird in the ne_a_t?

2. _____ Have you eve_n_ seen a tornado?

3. _____ The tornado l_o_ft a big mess.

4. _____ The me_t_ put the trash in trucks.

5. _____ _L_et those cups on the table.

6. _____ The little boy was _t_ext in line.

7. _____ He hid his hea_r_ behind his mom.

8. _____ The dog's back l_o_g is in a cast.

9. _____ I want to he_a_p those in need.

10. _____ Always do your very b_u_st.

☆ _____ I _l_ever want to be in a tornado.

☆ _____ They will build the houses _tr_ain.

☆ _____ This is the last seq_u_ence.

Word Bank

best	head	left	men	next	☆ again	☆ sentence
ever	help	leg	nest	set	☆ never	

G Dictation

Name _____

Listen and write the missing words.

1. _____ bird _____ _____ _____

   _____ I've _____ seen.

2. _____ _____ _____ _____ _____

   _____ door.

3. Daniel hurt ____ _____ _____ ____

   ____ _____ ___ fell.

EXAMINATION COPY

H Proofreading

One word in each set is misspelled. Fill in the oval by the misspelled word.

1. ◯ hed
   ◯ left
   ◯ nest

2. ◯ ask
   ◯ nexd
   ◯ camp

3. ◯ hat
   ◯ help
   ◯ mans

4. ◯ cet
   ◯ ever
   ◯ map

5. ◯ last
   ◯ lefd
   ◯ next

6. ◯ have
   ◯ set
   ◯ dest

⭐ ◯ agen
   ◯ apple
   ◯ bath

⭐ ◯ bath
   ◯ nevir
   ◯ asked

⭐ ◯ sintence
   ◯ apple
   ◯ asked

I Game

Name _____

Tommy, Daniel, and James will carry the supplies for the families and pets of Center City into the warehouse. You lead the way by moving one space each time you or your team spells a word correctly from this week's word list.

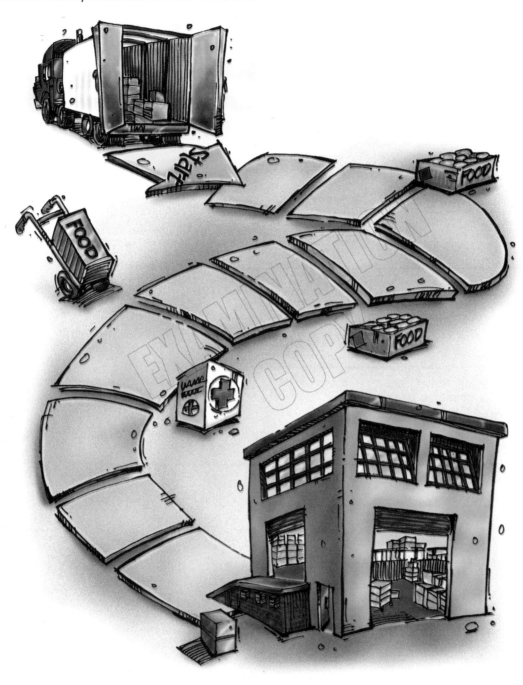

Remember: Little things done for others are very big to God.

J Journaling

Draw a picture in your journal of something you did to help someone else that made you feel great. Label your picture.

A Preview

Write each word as your teacher says it.

Name _____

1. _____

2. _____

3. _____

4. _____

5. _____

6. _____

7. _____

Challenge Words

8. _____

9. _____

10. _____

⭐ _____

⭐ _____

⭐ _____

Scripture

"Come to terms quickly ... before it is too late." Matt. 5:25

B **Word Shapes**   Name _____

Write each word in the correct word shape boxes. Then, in the word shape boxes, color the letter or letters that spell the sound of /i/ in each word. Circle the words in which the sound of /i/ is not spelled with **i**.

1. been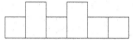

2. begin

3. digit

4. give

5. into

6. its

7. kid

8. live

9. quit

10. sister

☆ **Challenge**

Draw the correctly shaped boxes around each letter in these words.

b e c a u s e   g y m   u n t i l

C Hide and Seek

Name _____

Circle a cookie for each word you spell correctly.

D Other Word Forms

Using the words below, follow the instructions given by your teacher.

begins	lived
beginning	living
digits	quits
gives	quitting
giving	quitter
gyms	sisters
kids	
lives	

E Fun Ways to Spell

Initial the box of each activity you finish.

1.

Spell your words with puzzles…

2.

Spell your words on a paper chain …

3.

Spell your words out loud…

4.

Spell your words with split peas...

Words with /i/

Lesson

3

81

Write spelling words in place of the underlined word or words.

1. _____ The <u>number</u> you need to dial first is 9.

2. _____ Daniel is a nice <u>child</u> sometimes.

3. _____ Luke's <u>girl</u> <u>with</u> <u>the</u> <u>same</u> <u>parents</u> is Beth.

4. _____ Beth went <u>inside</u> the hospital to see Daniel.

5. _____ Have you <u>gone</u> to see Daniel?

6. _____ Daniel has a bandage and <u>the</u> <u>bandage's</u> color is white.

7. _____ The class will <u>hand over</u> a card to Daniel.

8. _____ <u>Stop</u> saying mean things to each other!

9. _____ Let's <u>start</u> by being kind to each other.

10. _____ <u>Dwell</u> in peace with each other.

⭐ _____ They weren't nice to each other <u>before</u> Daniel got hurt.

⭐ _____ Please glue this <u>since</u> it's broken.

⭐ _____ The class didn't go to the <u>play</u> <u>area</u> today.

Word Bank

been	digit	into	kid	quit	⭐ because	⭐ until
begin	give	its	live	sister	⭐ gym	

G Dictation

Name _____

Listen and write the missing words.

1. _____ calf _____ _____ calling _____

   _____ _____.

2. _____ _____ _____ _____ piano

   lessons soon.

3. Stephen _____ going _____ _____ room.

H Proofreading

One word in each set is misspelled. Fill in the oval by the misspelled word.

1. ◯ sistir
   ◯ give
   ◯ its

2. ◯ kid
   ◯ last
   ◯ beegin

3. ◯ men
   ◯ kwit
   ◯ best

4. ◯ deen
   ◯ live
   ◯ next

5. ◯ head
   ◯ intoo
   ◯ ever

6. ◯ dijit
   ◯ set
   ◯ help

⭐ ◯ jym
   ◯ never
   ◯ apple

⭐ ◯ sentence
   ◯ untill
   ◯ bath

⭐ ◯ again
   ◯ asked
   ◯ beecuz

I | Game

Help Beth take a big bunch of balloons to Daniel at the hospital. Draw one string in Beth's hand (and place a balloon at the top) each time you or your team spells a word correctly from this week's word list.

Remember: Solve your problems with others quickly.

J | Journaling

Draw a picture in your journal of some playground equipment you enjoy. Write two safety rules underneath the picture.

A Preview

Write each word as your teacher says it.

Name _____

1. _____

2. _____

3. _____

4. _____

5. _____

6. _____

7. _____

Challenge Words

8. _____

9. _____

10. _____

☆ _____

☆ _____

☆ _____

Scripture

"Live in peace with each other." Mark 9:50

Name _____

Write each word in the correct word shape boxes. Then, in the word shape boxes, color the letter that spells the sound of /o/ or /ô/ in each word. Circle the words that begin with the sound of /ô/.

1. box

2. dot

3. drop

4. frog

5. gone

6. lost

7. lot

8. odd

9. often

10. soft

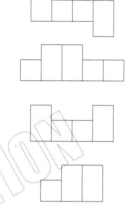
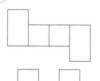

⭐ **Challenge**

Draw the correctly shaped boxes around each letter in these words.

forgot   job   tomorrow

C Hide and Seek

Circle a cookie for each word you spell correctly.

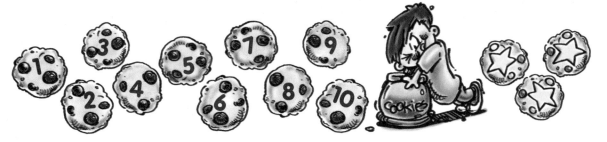

D Other Word Forms

Using the words below, follow the instructions given by your teacher.

boxes	frogs
boxed	jobs
boxing	lots
dots	softer
dotted	softest
dotting	softly
dropped	tomorrows
dropping	

E Fun Ways to Spell

Initial the box of each activity you finish.

1. ☐

Spell your words in your classmate's hand...

3. ☐

Spell your words out of the letter box...

2. ☐

Spell your words with paper cups...

4. ☐

Spell your words with shaving cream...

Name _____

Circle your spelling words in the puzzle. The words go across and down. Write each word in the correct blanks below.

Across

_____

_____

_____

_____

```
t  o  m  o  r  r  o  w  z
b  o  f  r  o  g  b  l  o
o  g  l  d  f  t  d  o  d
x  o  f  o  r  g  o  t  d
e  d  d  t  x  o  f  l  x
w  r  g  x  f  n  t  o  s
s  o  f  t  p  e  e  s  o
x  p  t  t  o  r  n  t  r
d  o  i  j  o  b  d  o  w
```

EXAMINATION COPY

Down

_____

_____

_____

_____

_____

_____

Word Bank

| box | drop | gone | lot | often | ⭐ forgot | ⭐ tomorrow |
| dot | frog | lost | odd | soft | ⭐ job | |

G Dictation

Name _____

Listen **and** write **the missing words.**

1. Kristin _____ ___ dime ___ _____

   parking ____.

2. _____ _____ _____ _____ ___ catch

   _____ flies.

3. _____ clay _____ ___ very

   ___ color.

H Proofreading

One word in each set is misspelled. Fill in the oval by the misspelled word.

1. ○ frog
   ○ dot
   ○ bocks

2. ○ lost
   ○ gon
   ○ sister

3. ○ od
   ○ head
   ○ lot

4. ○ than
   ○ quit
   ○ ofen

5. ○ best
   ○ live
   ○ sofd

6. ○ leg
   ○ brop
   ○ map

☆ ○ because
  ○ jod
  ○ sentence

☆ ○ tomorow
  ○ gym
  ○ never

☆ ○ bath
  ○ fergot
  ○ again

EXAMINATION COPY

I Game

Name _____

Place a game piece over each word your teacher says and spells. If the word appears on your card more than once, place a game piece over only one of the words. When you get five game pieces in a row, raise your hand and say, "Spelling is fun!"

FREE

Remember: When you do not feel like getting along with someone, you should choose to do it anyway.

J Journaling

Write a story in your journal about not feeling peaceful. Draw a picture of the last time you were not at peace with someone.

A Preview

Write each word as your teacher says it.

Name _____

1. _____

2. _____

3. _____

4. _____

5. _____

6. _____

7. _____

Challenge Words

☆ _____

8. _____

☆ _____

9. _____

☆ _____

10. _____

Scripture

"Be prepared, for you don't know what day your Lord is coming."
Matt. 24:42

B Word Shapes

Name _____

Write each word in the correct word shape boxes. Then, in the word shape boxes, color the letter or letters that spell the sound of /u/ in each word. Circle the words in which /u/ is spelled with **a** or **o**.

1. above

2. does

3. done

4. jump

5. just

6. must

7. none

8. number

9. sum

10. what

⭐ **Challenge**

Draw the correctly shaped boxes around each letter in these words.

bubble   once   sometimes

C Hide and Seek

Name _____

Circle a cookie for each word you spell correctly.

D Other Word Forms

Using the words below, follow the instructions given by your teacher.

bubbles   jumping

bubbled   sums

bubbling

numbers

numbered

numbering

jumps

jumped

E Fun Ways to Spell

Initial the box of each activity you finish.

1.

Spell your words with markers...

3.

Spell your words with snapping…

2.

Spell your words with letter tiles...

4.

Spell your words with finger paint…

Name _____

Place each set of word groups in order to write a sentence. Circle the spelling words.

Words with /u/

Lesson

5

Jesus coming ⚽ I must see ⚽ from above.

1. _____

Coach Larkin ⚽ What does ⚽ ask Tony ?

2. _____

up and ⚽ Just jump ⚽ hit the ball.

3. _____

When you are done ⚽ the number. ⚽ write

4. _____

of the sums ⚽ is right. ⚽ None

5. _____

we make ⚽ Sometimes ⚽ mistakes.

⭐ _____

want a ⚽ Tony does not ⚽ bubble bath.

⭐ _____

may play ⚽ Tony ⚽ once he cleans up.

⭐ _____

Word Bank						
above	done	just	none	sum	⭐ bubble	⭐ sometimes
does	jump	must	number	what	⭐ once	

94

G Dictation

Name _____

Listen and write the missing words.

1. _____ _____ over this rope.

2. _____ _____ _____ first _____ _____
_____ _____?

3. Christopher _____ _____ _____ _____
_____ chores yet.

4. _____ _____ _____ find _____ _____.

H Proofreading

One word in each set is misspelled. Fill in the oval by the misspelled word.

1. ◯ none
   ◯ whot
   ◯ jump

2. ◯ duz
   ◯ number
   ◯ soft

3. ◯ dun
   ◯ number
   ◯ just

4. ◯ drop
   ◯ nust
   ◯ camp

5. ◯ nest
   ◯ abuv
   ◯ set

6. ◯ som
   ◯ often
   ◯ frog

★ ◯ buble
   ◯ tomorrow
   ◯ until

★ ◯ again
   ◯ apple
   ◯ sumtimes

★ ◯ wunce
   ◯ because
   ◯ never

Run a drill through the cones with Tony or Stephen. Color one space for each word you or your team spells correctly from this week's word list.

Remember: Live as though Jesus were coming today.

J **Journaling**

Write a story in your journal about getting ready for Jesus to come.

A Test-Words

Name _____

Write each spelling word on the line as your teacher says it.

1. _____ 6. _____

2. _____ 7. _____

3. _____ 8. _____

4. _____ 9. _____

5. _____ 10. _____

B Test-Sentences

The two underlined words in each of the sentences are misspelled. Write the sentences on the lines below, spelling each underlined word correctly.

Show <u>Gawd's</u> love by the way you <u>liv</u>.

1. _____

Jesus was <u>gled</u> Rosa had <u>ben</u> kind.

2. _____

It is <u>tim</u> to <u>kwit</u>.

3. _____

☆ Test-Challenge Words

On a sheet of paper, write each challenge word as your teacher says it.

C Test-Dictation

Name _____

Listen and write the missing words.

1. _____ _____ piñata _____ _____?

2. _____ _____ _____ __ __ _____
right _____.

3. ___ _____ candy _____
__ _____ ground.

D Test-Proofreading

One word in each set is misspelled. Fill in the oval by the misspelled word.

1. ○ kamp
   ○ last
   ○ above

2. ○ been
   ○ min
   ○ next

3. ○ just
   ○ dijit
   ○ soft

4. ○ offen
   ○ sister
   ○ begin

5. ○ plan
   ○ have
   ○ numbr

6. ○ box
   ○ gone
   ○ od

7. ○ dott
   ○ drop
   ○ lot

8. ○ into
   ○ kib
   ○ live

9. ○ done
   ○ maq
   ○ hat

☆ Test-Challenge Words

On a sheet of paper, write each challenge word as your teacher says it.

98

Color each piece of candy on which the word is spelled incorrectly.

☆ **Test-Challenge Words**

On a sheet of paper, write each challenge word as your teacher says it.

Name _____

Rosa showed Jesus' love when she unselfishly bought her brother and sister lollipops at the grocery store. The kinds of lollipops they chose will be your team names for this game. Place a sticker each time you or your team spells a review word correctly.

Remember: Love others so they can see Jesus' love through you.

G Test-Words

Name _____

Write each spelling word on the line as your teacher says it.

1. _____   6. _____

2. _____   7. _____

3. _____   8. _____

4. _____   9. _____

5. _____   10. _____

H Test-Sentences

The two underlined words in each of the sentences are misspelled. Write the sentences on the lines below, spelling each underlined word correctly.

Rosa got a <u>nise</u> craft <u>cet</u>.

1. _____

Rosa's new <u>reb</u> shirt was very <u>souft</u>.

2. _____

Which <u>wun</u> do you like the <u>dest</u>?

3. _____

☆ Test-Challenge Words

On a sheet of paper, write each challenge word as your teacher says it.

Name _____

Write a paragraph telling how everyone will be able to see that you are Jesus' disciple by your actions. Write at least four sentences.

_____

_____

_____

_____

_____

_____

Scripture

"Your strong love for each other will prove to the world that you are my disciples."
John 13:35

Spelling Is Fun!

This certificate is awarded to

_____

for practicing the following words, by doing terrific spelling activities and playing great spelling games!

Date _____

add	best	been	box	above
ask	ever	begin	dot	does
camp	head	digit	drop	done
fast	help	give	frog	jump
hat	left	into	gone	just
have	leg	its	lost	must
last	men	kid	lot	none
map	nest	live	odd	number
plan	next	quit	often	sum
than	set	sister	soft	what
☆ apple	☆ again	☆ because	☆ forgot	☆ bubble
☆ asked	☆ never	☆ gym	☆ job	☆ once
☆ bath	☆ sentence	☆ until	☆ tomorrow	☆ sometimes

A Reason For SPELLING

A Reason For Spelling®

Dear Parent,

   We are about to begin a new spelling unit containing five weekly lessons. A set of ten words plus three challenge words will be studied each week. All the words will be reviewed in the sixth week.

   Values based on the Scriptures listed below will be taught in each lesson.

Lesson 7	Lesson 8	Lesson 9	Lesson 10	Lesson 11
bake	be	buy	boat	blow
cake	clean	cry	cold	grow
came	east	dry	hold	know
game	even	fly	home	low
gate	he's	I'm	hope	own
gave	keep	light	most	row
grade	people	might	old	slow
late	read	night	road	snow
name	tree	right	roll	throw
page	we'll	tie	told	tow
☆ break	☆ between	☆ Bible	☆ don't	☆ below
☆ great	☆ Jesus	☆ child	☆ over	☆ mowing
☆ obey	☆ sleep	☆ high	☆ wrote	☆ snowman

Mark 5:19   Luke 11:36   Luke 1:46, 47   Matt. 22:39   Luke 21:33

A Preview

Write each word as your teacher says it.

Name _____

1. _____

2. _____

3. _____

4. _____

5. _____

6. _____

7. _____

8. _____

9. _____

10. _____

Challenge Words

⭐ _____

⭐ _____

⭐ _____

Scripture

"Go home to your friends ... and tell them what wonderful things God has done for you." Mark 5:19

Write each word in the correct word shape boxes. Then, in the word shape boxes, color the letters that spell the sound of /ā/ in each word. Circle the word that begins with the consonant cluster **gr**.

1. bake

2. cake

3. came

4. game

5. gate

6. gave

7. grade

8. late

9. name

10. page

☆ **Challenge**

Draw the correctly shaped boxes around each letter in these words.

break   great   obey

C Hide and Seek

Name _____

Circle a cookie for each word you spell correctly.

D Other Word Forms

Using the words below, follow the instructions given by your teacher.

bakes	graded	pages
baked	grading	
baking	grader	
cakes	later	
caked	latest	
games	names	
gates	named	
grades	naming	

E Fun Ways to Spell

Initial the box of each activity you finish.

1. ☐

Spell your words with crayon…

2. ☐

Spell your words with sidewalk chalk…

3. ☐

Spell your words with rhythm instruments…

4. ☐

Spell your words with cotton balls...

107

Name _____

Write each set of spelling words in alphabetical order.

1. gate   _____

late   _____

grade   _____

2. came   _____

bake   _____

cake   _____

3. game   _____

name   _____

page   _____

4. gave   _____

came   _____

grade   _____

☆ obey   _____

break   _____

great   _____

A B C D E F G H I J K L M N O P Q R S T U V W X Y Z

a b c d e f g h i j k l m n o p q r s t u v w x y z

G Dictation

Name _____

Listen and write the missing words.

1. Setsuko _____ ___ ____ _____.

2. ____ ____ leaped over ____ _____.

3. Katelynn wrote ____ _____ ___

____ _____ _____.

4. ____ teacher _____ each student

___ _____.

H Proofreading

One word in each set is misspelled. Fill in the oval by the misspelled word.

1. ◯ gate
   ◯ paje
   ◯ digit

2. ◯ kame
   ◯ gave
   ◯ its

3. ◯ gane
   ◯ kid
   ◯ grade

4. ◯ give
   ◯ name
   ◯ laete

5. ◯ add
   ◯ dake
   ◯ odd

6. ◯ kake
   ◯ been
   ◯ late

⭐ ◯ obay
   ◯ gym
   ◯ bubble

⭐ ◯ forgot
   ◯ sometimes
   ◯ brack

⭐ ◯ grat
   ◯ because
   ◯ job

I Game

Name _____

Get in line to ride the Firebird Roller Coaster. Move up in line one space for each word you or your team spells correctly from this week's word list.

Remember: Praise God for each special thing He does for you.

J Journaling

Write three sentences in your journal about what wonderful things God has done for you.

A Preview

Name _____

Write each word as your teacher says it.

1. _____

2. _____

3. _____

4. _____

5. _____

6. _____

7. _____

8. _____

9. _____

10. _____

Challenge Words

☆ _____

☆ _____

☆ _____

Scripture

"If you are filled with light within ... then your face will be radiant too."
Luke 11:36

B **Word Shapes**   Name _____

Write each word in the correct word shape boxes. Then, in the word shape boxes, color the letter or letters that spell the sound of /ē/ in each word. Circle the words that are contractions. Draw a line under the words that begin with the consonant clusters **cl** or **tr**.

1. be

2. clean

3. east

4. even

5. he's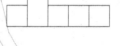

6. keep

7. people

8. read

9. tree

10. we'll

⭐ **Challenge**

Draw the correctly shaped boxes around each letter in these words.

b e t w e e n   J e s u s   s l e e p

C | Hide and Seek

Circle a cookie for each word you spell correctly.

D | Other Word Forms

Using the words below, follow the instructions given by your teacher.

been	evening	sleeps
cleans	uneven	slept
cleaned	keeps	sleeping
cleaning	kept	trees
cleaner	keeping	
cleanest	reads	
unclean	reading	
eastern	reader	

E | Fun Ways to Spell

Initial the box of each activity you finish.

1. ☐

Spell your words with an eraser…

3. ☐

Spell your words with clapping…

2. ☐

Spell your words with paint...

4. ☐

Spell your words in wet sand…

F **Clues**

Name _____

Use the clues to write the spelling words.

1. _____ he is

2. _____ we will

3. _____ not odd

4. _____ not dirty

5. _____ human beings

6. _____ fulfill, like a promise

7. _____ exist or to take place

8. _____ a tall plant with a trunk

9. _____ face this way to see the sun rise

10. _____ know what written words mean

☆ _____ in the middle of

☆ _____ to take a nap

☆ _____ the Son of God

Word Bank

be	east	he's	people	tree	☆ between	☆ sleep
clean	even	keep	read	we'll	☆ Jesus	

G Dictation

Name _____

Listen and write the missing words.

1. _____ _____ like ___ _____

   ____ newspaper.

2. _____ _____ ___ _____ towels

   ___ here.

3. _____ climbing ___ ___ ___.

4. _____ sure ___ feed ___ ___.

H Proofreading

One word in each set is misspelled. Fill in the oval by the misspelled word.

1. ◯ bake
   ◯ cleen
   ◯ we'll

2. ◯ live
   ◯ soft
   ◯ de

3. ◯ done
   ◯ leg
   ◯ peepl

4. ◯ reab
   ◯ even
   ◯ tree

5. ◯ late
   ◯ eest
   ◯ he's

6. ◯ keap
   ◯ set
   ◯ head

⭐ ◯ job
   ◯ betwean
   ◯ once

⭐ ◯ jesus
   ◯ obey
   ◯ because

⭐ ◯ forgot
   ◯ never
   ◯ sleap

115

I Game

Name _____

Retrace Christopher's path the day he broke his arm. Move one space each time you or your team spells a word correctly from this week's word list.

Remember: Let your face show that Jesus lives in your heart.

J Journaling

Write your own prayer in your journal asking God to fill you with His love so everyone can see it like a light on your face.

A Preview

Write each word as your teacher says it.

Name _____

1. _____

2. _____

3. _____

4. _____

5. _____

6. _____

7. _____

8. _____

9. _____

10. _____

Challenge Words

☆ _____

☆ _____

☆ _____

Scripture

"Oh, how I praise the Lord. How I rejoice in God my Savior!"
Luke 1:46, 47

B Word Shapes

Name _____

Write each word in the correct word shape boxes. Then, in the word shape boxes, color the letter or letters that spell the sound of /ī/ in each word. Circle the word that has a contraction. Draw a line under the silent letters **gh**.

1. buy

2. cry

3. dry

4. fly

5. I'm

6. light

7. might

8. night

9. right

10. tie

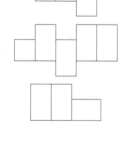

⭐ **Challenge**

Draw the correctly shaped boxes around each letter in these words.

Bible   child   high

118

C Hide and Seek

Name _____

Circle a cookie for each word you spell correctly.

D Other Word Forms

Using the words below, follow the instructions given by your teacher.

Bibles	dries	I	mightiest
buys	dried	lights	nights
bought	drying	lighted	nightly
buying	flies	lighting	rights
children	flew	lighter	ties
cries	flying	lightest	tied
cried	higher	mighty	tying
crying	highest	mightier	

E Fun Ways to Spell

Initial the box of each activity you finish.

1.

Spell your words with puzzles…

3.

Spell your words out loud…

2.

Spell your words on a paper chain …

4.

Spell your words with split peas...

119

F **Words in Sentences**

Name _____

Use the shapes to find the word to complete each sentence. Write it in the blank.

 1. It _____ start to rain soon.

 2. Turn the playroom _____ on.

 3. Always make the _____ choice.

 4. It may rain all _____.

 5. You _____ when you feel sad.

 6. This ball can really _____.

 7. You need to _____ your shoe.

 8. The umbrella keeps you _____.

 9. They will _____ a new monitor.

 10. _____ glad God saves me!

Word Bank

 dry night buy light cry right

might fly tie I'm

G Dictation

Listen and write the missing words.

1. _____ going ____ _____ _____ dishes.

2. ____ _____ ____ my kite today.

3. _____ street _____ comes _____

____ _____.

4. Rosa wants ____ _____ ____ doll _____

____ ____.

H Proofreading

One word in each set is misspelled. Fill in the oval by the misspelled word.

1. ⬭ nest
   ⬭ kry
   ⬭ I'm

2. ⬭ nite
   ⬭ gave
   ⬭ gone

3. ⬭ fly
   ⬭ tye
   ⬭ live

4. ⬭ duy
   ⬭ right
   ⬭ than

5. ⬭ migt
   ⬭ begin
   ⬭ sum

6. ⬭ bry
   ⬭ light
   ⬭ left

⭐ ⬭ apple
   ⬭ chid
   ⬭ great

⭐ ⬭ gym
   ⬭ bible
   ⬭ sentence

⭐ ⬭ break
   ⬭ tomorrow
   ⬭ hy

I Game

Daniel and Tommy made a poor choice to throw the ball inside the house. Follow the path of the baseball toward the computer monitor. Color one space for each word you or your team spells correctly from this week's word list.

Remember: God always loves us and wants to forgive us.

J Journaling

Write at least four sentences in your journal about a time when you were in trouble and needed help.

A Preview

Write each word as your teacher says it.

Name _____

1. _____

2. _____

3. _____

4. _____

5. _____

6. _____

7. _____

8. _____

9. _____

10. _____

Challenge Words

⭐ _____

⭐ _____

⭐ _____

Scripture

"Love your neighbor as much as you love yourself." Matt. 22:39

Name _____

Write each word in the correct word shape boxes. Then, in the word shape boxes, color the letter or letters that spell the sound of /ō/ in each word. Circle the words in which /ō/ is spelled with **o-e**. Draw a line under the words in which /ō/ is spelled with **oa**.

1. boat

2. cold

3. hold

4. home

5. hope

6. most

7. old

8. road

9. roll

10. told

☆ **Challenge**

Draw the correctly shaped boxes around each letter in these words.

don't   over   wrote

C Hide and Seek

Name _____

Circle a cookie for each word you spell correctly.

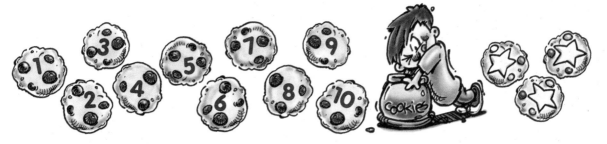

D Other Word Forms

Using the words below, follow the instructions given by your teacher.

boats	hopes	overly	telling
boating	hoped	roads	
colder	hoping	rolls	
coldest	hopeful	rolled	
holds	hopeless	rolling	
held	mostly	roller	
holding	older	tell	
homes	oldest	tells	

E Fun Ways to Spell

Initial the box of each activity you finish.

1.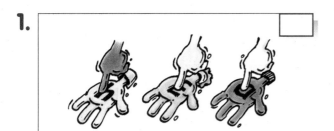

Spell your words in your classmate's hand...

3.

Spell your words out of the letter box...

2.

Spell your words with paper cups...

4.

Spell your words with shaving cream...

125

Use the puzzle clues to write the spelling words.

Across

1. Not hot
2. I tell today, I _____ yesterday.
4. more than anything else
6. place where you live
8. to grab something and not let go

Down

3. This is a yummy sweet _____.
5. We drive down the _____.
7. travels on water
8. a feeling that things will get better
9. not young

Word Bank

boat	hold	hope	old	roll
cold	home	most	road	told

G Dictation

Name _____

Listen and write the missing words.

1. _____ _____ _____ ____ bumpy.

2. Tony _____ _____ _____ _____

_____ carefully.

3. _____ enjoyed _____ _____

_____ _____.

4. ___ _____ _____ water ___ ____ _____.

H Proofreading

One word in each set is misspelled. Fill in the oval by the misspelled word.

1. ◯ bote
   ◯ most
   ◯ hat

2. ◯ fast
   ◯ hoam
   ◯ road

3. ◯ best
   ◯ tree
   ◯ haop

4. ◯ dot
   ◯ must
   ◯ odl

5. ◯ next
   ◯ rol
   ◯ light

6. ◯ kold
   ◯ hold
   ◯ told

⭐ ◯ ovr
   ◯ bath
   ◯ sometimes

⭐ ◯ until
   ◯ never
   ◯ bon't

⭐ ◯ again
   ◯ asked
   ◯ roet

I | Game

Name _____

Place a game piece over each word your teacher says and spells. If the word appears on your card more than once, place a game piece over only one of the words. When you get five game pieces in a row, raise your hand and say, "Spelling is fun!"

Remember: Do kind things for others as often as you do them for yourself.

J | Journaling

Make a list in your journal of at least seven ways your actions can show you love your neighbor as much as you love yourself.

A Preview

Write each word as your teacher says it.

1. _____

2. _____

3. _____

4. _____

5. _____

6. _____

7. _____

8. _____

9. _____

10. _____

Challenge Words

☆ _____

☆ _____

☆ _____

Scripture

"Though all heaven and earth shall pass away, yet my words remain forever true."
Luke 21:33

B Word Shapes

Write each word in the correct word shape boxes. Then, in the word shape boxes, color the letters that spell the sound of /ō/ in each word. Circle the words that begin with a consonant cluster.

Words with /ō/

Lesson
11

1. blow

2. grow

3. know

4. low

5. own

6. row

7. slow

8. snow

9. throw

10. tow

⭐ Challenge

Draw the correctly shaped boxes around each letter in these words.

below   mowing   snowman

130

C Hide and Seek

Circle a cookie for each word you spell correctly.

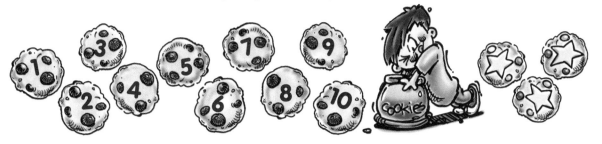

D Other Word Forms

Using the words below, follow the instructions given by your teacher.

throws	owns	growing
throwing	owned	slower
towed	owner	slowest
mow	snows	slowing
mows	snowed	knows
mowed	snowing	
blowing	lower	
rows	lowest	

E Fun Ways to Spell

Initial the box of each activity you finish.

1.

Spell your words with markers...

3.

Spell your words with snapping...

2.

Spell your words with letter tiles...

4.

Spell your words with finger paint...

131

F **Unscramble Words**

Name _____

Change the scrambled letters to write your spelling words in the blanks. Trace Beth's path through Grandpa's flower garden by following your scrambled spelling words.

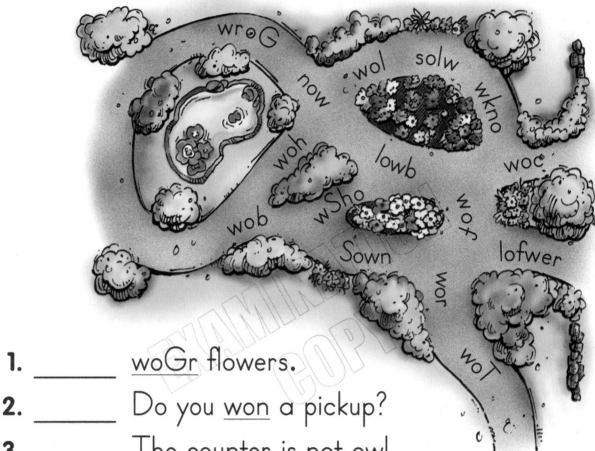

1. _____ <u>woGr</u> flowers.

2. _____ Do you <u>won</u> a pickup?

3. _____ The counter is not <u>owl</u>.

4. _____ Hill's pickup is not <u>wslo</u>.

5. _____ I <u>owkn</u> Jesus loves you.

6. _____ Dust will <u>lobw</u> across the field.

7. _____ <u>hTorw</u> the seeds on the ground.

8. _____ <u>wSno</u> is cold and white.

9. _____ Grandpa's tools were in a <u>orw</u>.

10. _____ <u>wTo</u> the pickup back to the farm.

Word Bank

blow	know	own	slow	throw
grow	low	row	snow	tow

G Dictation

Listen and write the missing words.

1. Show ___ ___ ___ ___ ___ ___ .

2. ___ ___ ___ ___ ___ plant ___ ___?

3. Tommy ___ ___ ___ bubble ___ ___ ___ .

4. ___ ___ shovel ___ ___ ___ .

H Proofreading

One word in each set is misspelled. Fill in the oval by the misspelled word.

1. ◯ best
◯ thro
◯ blow

2. ◯ slow
◯ row
◯ jrow

3. ◯ cry
◯ kno
◯ road

4. ◯ digit
◯ kid
◯ sno

5. ◯ oan
◯ number
◯ tow

6. ◯ men
◯ loe
◯ light

⭐ ◯ sleep
◯ child
◯ beelo

⭐ ◯ Bible
◯ mowig
◯ job

⭐ ◯ wrote
◯ gym
◯ snoman

133

I Game

Name _____

Take a walk with Beth as she enjoys memories of times shared with her grandpa. Move one space for each word you or your team spells correctly from this week's word list.

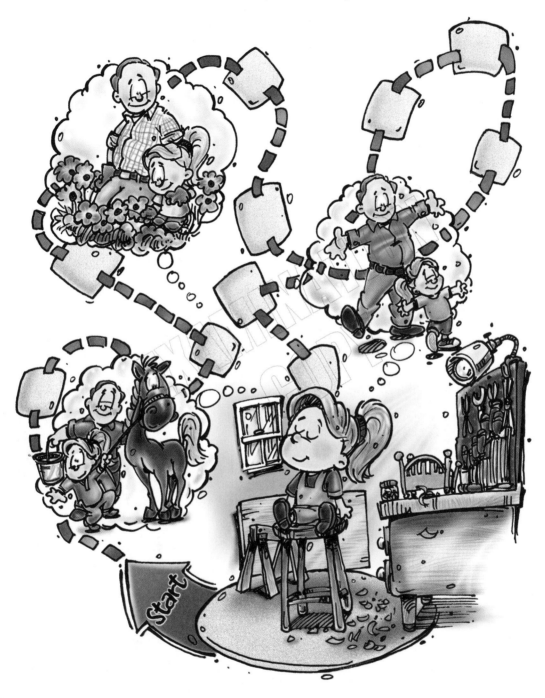

Remember: No matter what happens, God never changes.

J Journaling

Write in your journal about a time you felt very sad.

A Test-Words

Name _____

Write each spelling word on the line as your teacher says it.

1. _____   1. _____

2. _____   2. _____

3. _____   3. _____

4. _____   4. _____

5. _____   5. _____

B Test-Sentences

The two underlined words in each of the sentences are misspelled. Write the sentences on the lines below, spelling each underlined word correctly.

I <u>wil</u> help <u>cleen</u> out the garage.

1. _____

There are <u>mor</u> cookies to <u>baek</u>.

2. _____

Did <u>yu</u> <u>gro</u> an inch this year?

3. _____

☆ Test-Challenge Words

On a sheet of paper, write each challenge word as your teacher says it.

C Test-Dictation

Listen and write the missing words.

Name _____

1. _____ going ____ _____

    ____ _____.

2. ___ _____ ____ _____ ____ _____

    ____ ___.

3. ____ _____ _____ ____ _____ _____.

D Test-Proofreading

One word in each set is misspelled. Fill in the oval by the misspelled word.

1. ○ oald
   ○ light
   ○ throw

2. ○ gaim
   ○ boat
   ○ gate

3. ○ snow
   ○ flie
   ○ read

4. ○ grade
   ○ might
   ○ toald

5. ○ loe
   ○ late
   ○ tree

6. ○ I'm
   ○ people
   ○ nam

7. ○ tye
   ○ tow
   ○ road

8. ○ gave
   ○ rolle
   ○ we'll

9. ○ slow
   ○ oane
   ○ east

☆ **Test-Challenge Words**

On a sheet of paper, write each challenge word as your teacher says it.

Color each train car on which the word is spelled incorrectly.

even i'm gaet bote

cake raed liht mots

thro gaev trea lat dry

cold buy peepel ro

☆ **Test-Challenge Words**

On a sheet of paper, write each challenge word as your teacher says it.

F **Game**

Name _____

God made corn and grapes, and there are lots of good things we can make out of them like corn flakes, corn chips, and raisins. Use these as your team names for this game. Place a sticker each time you or your team spells a review word correctly.

Remember: Choose to use for good the wonderful things God has made.

G Test-Words

Name _____

Write each spelling word on the line as your teacher says it.

1. _____   6. _____

2. _____   7. _____

3. _____   8. _____

4. _____   9. _____

5. _____   10. _____

H Test-Sentences

The two underlined words in each of the sentences are misspelled. Write the sentences on the lines below, spelling each underlined word correctly.

I can <u>ried</u> my bike on this <u>raod</u>.

1. _____

The sky was a deep <u>bloo</u> last <u>nite</u>.

2. _____

You may take the <u>bal</u> <u>hoam</u>.

3. _____

☆ Test-Challenge Words

On a sheet of paper, write each challenge word as your teacher says it.

I Writing Assessment

Write five sentences about why it is important for you not to drink alcohol.

Name _____

_____

_____

_____

_____

_____

_____

_____

_____

Scripture

"He created everything there is—nothing exists that he didn't make."
John 1:3

Spelling Is Fun!

This certificate is awarded to

_____

for practicing the following words, by doing terrific
spelling activities and playing great spelling games!

Date _____

bake	be	buy	boat	blow
cake	clean	cry	cold	grow
came	east	dry	hold	know
game	even	fly	home	low
gate	he's	I'm	hope	own
gave	keep	light	most	row
grade	people	might	old	slow
late	read	night	road	snow
name	tree	right	roll	throw
page	we'll	tie	told	tow
☆ break	☆ between	☆ Bible	☆ don't	☆ below
☆ great	☆ Jesus	☆ child	☆ over	☆ mowing
☆ obey	☆ sleep	☆ high	☆ wrote	☆ snowman

Dear Parent,

We are about to begin a new spelling unit containing five weekly lessons. A set of ten words plus three challenge words will be studied each week. All the words will be reviewed in the sixth week.

Values based on the Scriptures listed below will be taught in each lesson.

Lesson 13	Lesson 14	Lesson 15	Lesson 16	Lesson 17
paint	arm	air	bird	any
pay	barn	bear	circle	baby
plays	car	eye	color	every
pray	card	fine	first	family
rain	dark	fire	purple	holy
say	far	like	under	only
stay	farm	line	water	penny
today	hard	their	were	ready
train	part	where	word	story
way	yard	write	work	very
☆ birthday	☆ heart	☆ beside	☆ heard	☆ city
☆ praise	☆ large	☆ care	☆ third	☆ easy
☆ stayed	☆ party	☆ while	☆ world	☆ study
Matt. 16:24	Luke 6:37	John 18:37	Luke 4:8	Luke 1:68

A Preview

Write each word as your teacher says it.

Name _____

1. _____

2. _____

3. _____

4. _____

5. _____

6. _____

7. _____

8. _____

9. _____

10. _____

Challenge Words

⭐ _____

⭐ _____

⭐ _____

Scripture

"If anyone wants to be a follower of mine, let him ... take up his cross and follow me." Matt. 16:24

Write each word in the correct word shape boxes. Then, in the word shape boxes, color the letters that spell the sound of **/ā/** in each word. Circle the words that begin with a consonant cluster.

1. paint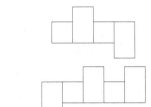

2. pay

3. plays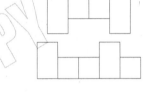

4. pray

5. rain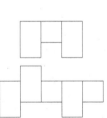

6. say

7. stay

8. today

9. train

10. way

⭐ **Challenge**

Draw the correctly shaped boxes around each letter in these words.

b i r t h d a y   p r a i s e   s t a y e d

C Hide and Seek

Name _____

Circle a cookie for each word you spell correctly.

D Other Word Forms

Using the words below, follow the instructions given by your teacher.

birthdays	played	praying	saying
paints	playing	prayer	stays
painted	player	rains	stayed
painting	praises	rained	staying
painter	praised	raining	trains
pays	praising	rainy	ways
paid	prays	says	
paying	prayed	said	

E Fun Ways to Spell

Initial the box of each activity you finish.

1.

Spell your words with crayon…

3.

Spell your words with rhythm instruments…

2.

Spell your words with stencils…

4.

Spell your words with cotton balls...

145

Name _____

Write **each set of spelling words in alphabetical order.**

1. plays, say, rain

_____ _____ _____

2. way, train, pray

_____ _____ _____

3. stay, pay, today

_____ _____ _____

4. rain, paint, way

_____ _____ _____

5. train, stay, plays

_____ _____ _____

6. way, today, pray

_____ _____ _____

7. paint, say, rain

_____ _____ _____

8. way, train, pay

_____ _____ _____

9. say, plays, today

_____ _____ _____

10. rain, paint, stay

_____ _____ _____

A B C D E F G H I J K L M N O P Q R S T U V W X Y Z

a b c d e f g h i j k l m n o p q r s t u v w x y z

G Dictation

Name _____

Listen and write the missing words.

1. _____ want ____ _____ _____

_____ _____.

2. _____ farmers _____ ____ _____.

3. Rosa _____ _____ _____ _____.

4. Which _____ _____ _____

___ ___?

H Proofreading

One word in each set is misspelled. Fill in the oval by the misspelled word.

1. ○ page
   ○ paitn
   ○ way

2. ○ sey
   ○ know
   ○ clean

3. ○ pray
   ○ keep
   ○ playz

4. ○ grow
   ○ stay
   ○ tooday

5. ○ trane
   ○ what
   ○ most

6. ○ people
   ○ rane
   ○ pay

⭐ ○ staed
   ○ Bible
   ○ gym

⭐ ○ don't
   ○ below
   ○ praez

⭐ ○ wrote
   ○ berthday
   ○ high

I | Game

Name _____

Tommy and Lisa's dad made stew for supper while their mom was away helping their grandmother. Be the first to the dinner table by moving one space each time you or your team spells a word correctly from this week's word list.

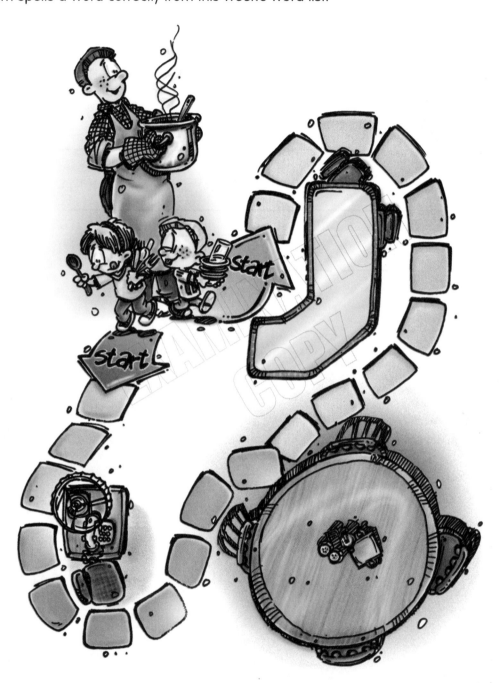

Remember: Follow Jesus by doing what He would do.

J | Journaling

Write a promise to God in your journal that you will be His follower even when it's not easy to do. Underneath your promise, draw a picture of yourself.

A Preview

Write each word as your teacher says it.

Name _____

1. _____

2. _____

3. _____

4. _____

5. _____

6. _____

7. _____

8. _____

9. _____

10. _____

Challenge Words

⭐ _____

⭐ _____

⭐ _____

Scripture

"Never criticize—or condemn or it will all come back on you." Luke 6:37

B Word Shapes

Name _____

Write each word in the correct word shape boxes. Then, in the word shape boxes, color the letters that spell the sound of **/är/** in each word.

1. arm

2. barn

3. car

4. card

5. dark

6. far

7. farm

8. hard

9. part

10. yard

⭐ **Challenge**

Draw the correctly shaped boxes around each letter in these words.

heart   large   party

C Hide and Seek

Circle a cookie for each word you spell correctly.

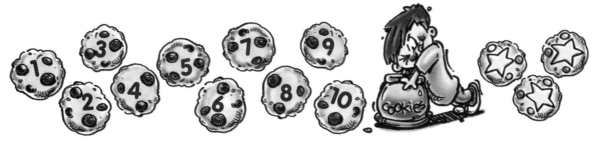

D Other Word Forms

Using the words below, follow the instructions given by your teacher.

arms	farther	hearts	yards
armed	farthest	larger	
armful	farms	largest	
barns	farmed	parts	
cards	farming	parted	
cars	harder	parting	
darker	hardest	parties	
darkest	hardly	impart	

E Fun Ways to Spell

Initial the box of each activity you finish.

1.

Spell your words with an eraser…

3.

Spell your words with clapping…

2.

Spell your words with paint...

4.

Spell your words in wet sand…

F Rhyme Time

Name _____

Write the spelling words that rhyme.

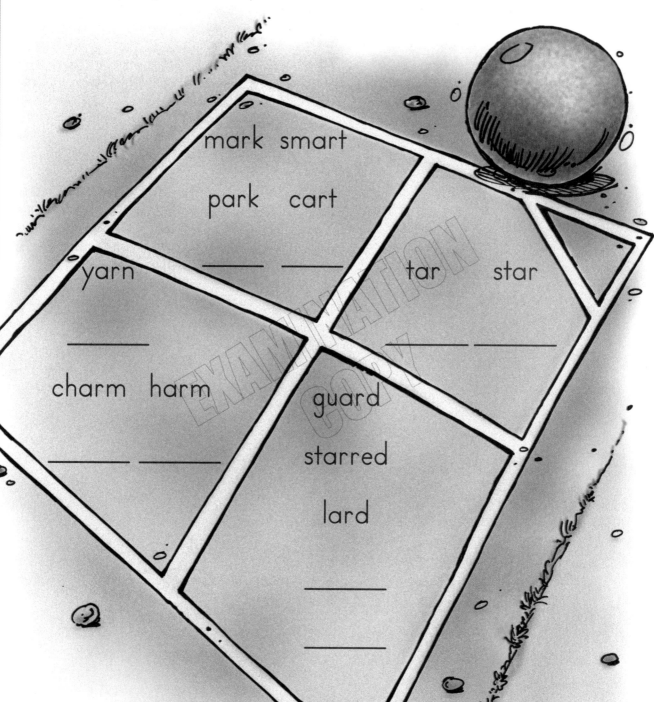

mark   smart

park   cart

yarn   _____   _____

_____

charm   harm

_____   _____

tar   star

_____   _____

guard

starred

lard

_____

_____

_____

Word Bank

arm	car	dark	farm	part
barn	card	far	hard	yard

G Dictation

Name _____

Listen and write the missing words.

1. _____ _____ _____ _____ _____

   _____ _____ _____.

2. _____ can't _____ _____ _____

   _____ _____ _____.

3. _____ _____ _____ _____ _____

   _____ here?

H Proofreading

One word in each set is misspelled. Fill in the oval by the misspelled word.

1. ◯ say
   ◯ own
   ◯ darck

2. ◯ today
   ◯ harb
   ◯ far

3. ◯ east
   ◯ qart
   ◯ tow

4. ◯ yarb
   ◯ arm
   ◯ boat

5. ◯ kar
   ◯ rain
   ◯ barn

6. ◯ might
   ◯ kard
   ◯ farm

 ◯ partie
   ◯ over
   ◯ sleep

 ◯ praise
   ◯ snowman
   ◯ larj

⭐ ◯ mowing
   ◯ haert
   ◯ stayed

153

I | Game

Name _____

Kristin wants to apologize to Setsuko for her unkind words. Lead the way by moving one space each time you or your team spells a word correctly from this week's word list.

Remember: Before you say something unkind about someone, think how you would feel if the unkind words were about you.

J | Journaling

What do you think Kristin should do about hurting Setsuko's feelings? Write your ideas down in your journal.

A Preview

Write each word as your teacher says it.

Name _____

1. _____

2. _____

3. _____

4. _____

5. _____

6. _____

7. _____

8. _____

9. _____

10. _____

Challenge Words

☆ _____

☆ _____

☆ _____

Scripture

"I came to bring truth to the world. All who love the truth are my followers." John 18:37

Name _____

Write each word in the correct word shape boxes. Then, in the word shape boxes, color the letters that spell the sound of /âr/ or /ī/ in each word. Circle the words that begin with the digraph **th** or **wh**.

1. air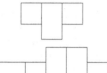

2. bear

3. eye

4. fine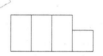

5. fire

6. like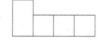

7. line

8. their

9. where

10. write

⭐ **Challenge**

Draw the correctly shaped boxes around each letter in these words.

beside   care   while

156

C Hide and Seek

Name _____

Circle a cookie for each word you spell correctly.

D Other Word Forms

Using the words below, follow the instructions given by your teacher.

airs	caring	fired	theirs
aired	eyes	firing	writes
airing	eyed	likes	writing
bears	eyeing	liked	writer
bearing	fines	liking	
besides	fined	lines	
cares	fining	lined	
cared	fires	lining	

E Fun Ways to Spell

Initial the box of each activity you finish.

1.

Spell your words with puzzles…

3.

Spell your words out loud…

2.

Spell your words on a paper chain …

4.

Spell your words with split peas...

F **Word Change**   Name _____

Write a spelling word in place of the underlined word or words.

1. All the desks were in a <u>row</u>. _____

2. The <u>brown furry animal</u> is cute and mean. _____

3. <u>Tony and Stephen's</u> favorite game is dodge ball. _____

4. <u>At what place</u> did they leave the jump ropes? _____

5. <u>Print</u> your name here. _____

6. It is always <u>okay</u> to tell the truth. _____

7. The ball flew through <u>what we breathe</u>. _____

8. Tony did not want to look Mrs. Morgan in the <u>seeing part of her face</u>. _____

9. Lies grow like a wild <u>red hot flame</u>. _____

10. Tony does not <u>enjoy</u> eating carrots. _____

⭐ <u>At the same time</u> he played, everyone ate lunch. _____

⭐ She will <u>mind</u> if you leave the ropes out. _____

⭐ The trash can was <u>next to</u> the door. _____

Word Bank						
air	eye	fire	line	where	⭐ beside	⭐ while
bear	fine	like	their	write	⭐ care	

G Dictation

Name _____

Listen and write the missing words.

1. Sarah _____ ___ ___ _____ letters.

2. _____ _____ ___ _____ _____ _____ .

3. Grandpa built ___ _____ _____
   _____ _____ .

4. _____ _____ _____ coats?

H Proofreading

One word in each set is misspelled. Fill in the oval by the misspelled word.

1. ○ kid
   ○ dark
   ○ ther

2. ○ road
   ○ ayr
   ○ stay

3. ○ wriet
   ○ tree
   ○ line

4. ○ hard
   ○ baer
   ○ eye

5. ○ number
   ○ fier
   ○ cold

6. ○ wher
   ○ fine
   ○ paint

⭐ ○ large
   ○ beeside
   ○ stayed

⭐ ○ cair
   ○ party
   ○ forgot

⭐ ○ heart
   ○ whiel
   ○ between

I | Game

Tony wants to obey the class rule and take home the part of his lunch he did not eat. Help Tony get his uneaten lunch out of the trash can. Move one space for each word you or your team spells correctly.

Remember: Be honest and others will know you love Jesus.

J | Journaling

Make a list in your journal of five people whom you can trust to always tell you the truth. Label the list: **Truth Lovers**.

A Preview

Write each word as your teacher says it.

Name _____

1. _____

2. _____

3. _____

4. _____

5. _____

6. _____

7. _____

8. _____

9. _____

10. _____

Challenge Words

 _____

 _____

 _____

Scripture

"We must worship God, and him alone. So it is written in the Scriptures."
Luke 4:8

Name _____

Write each word in the correct word shape boxes. Then, in the word shape boxes, color the letters that spell the sound of /ûr/ or /ər/ in each word. Circle the words which have two syllables.

1. bird

2. circle

3. color

4. first

5. purple

6. under

7. water

8. were

9. word

10. work

⭐ **Challenge**

Draw the correctly shaped boxes around each letter in these words.

heard   third   world

C Hide and Seek

Circle a cookie for each word you spell correctly.

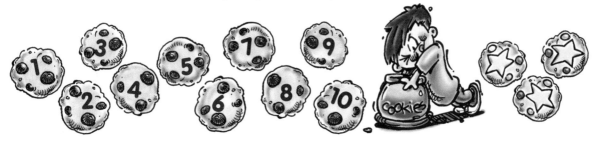

D Other Word Forms

Using the words below, follow the instructions given by your teacher.

birds	thirds	worked
circles	waters	working
circled	watered	worlds
circling	watering	
colors	words	
colored	worded	
coloring	wording	
purples	works	

E Fun Ways to Spell

Initial the box of each activity you finish.

1.

Spell your words in your classmate's hand...

3.

Spell your words out of the letter box...

2.

Spell your words with paper cups...

4.

Spell your words with shaving cream...

Change the underlined letter or letters, and write the spelling word in the blank.

Words with /ûr/ or /er/

Lesson
16

1. Sarah's eyes <u>th</u>ere wet. _____
2. The girls were in a circ<u>us</u>
   around Katelynn's desk. _____
3. The Bible is God's <u>c</u>ord. _____
4. The <u>th</u>ird is in its cage. _____
5. Keep God <u>th</u>irst in your life. _____
6. Drink lots of <u>l</u>ater every day. _____
7. The co<u>v</u>er of Katie's hair is black. _____
8. They will <u>f</u>ork for the kids in Malawi. _____
9. The dancing dragon tunic is not pu<u>dd</u>le. _____
10. Sarah had dirt <u>wo</u>nder her fingernails. _____
⭐ Girls all over the work<u>s</u> love dolls. _____
⭐ Katelynn is thir<u>st</u>. _____
⭐ She <u>b</u>eard Katelynn liked dolls. _____

Word Bank						
bird	color	purple	water	word	⭐ heard	⭐ world
circle	first	under	were	work	⭐ third	

G Dictation

Listen and write the missing words.

1. _____ _____ _____ built _____

   _____ _____ .

2. Please _____ _____ _____ _____ .

3. Stephen, _____ _____ swimming _____

   _____ _____ ?

H Proofreading

One word in each set is misspelled. Fill in the oval by the misspelled word.

1. ○ coler
   ○ train
   ○ say

2. ○ work
   ○ purpel
   ○ yard

3. ○ woter
   ○ often
   ○ jump

4. ○ their
   ○ were
   ○ werd

5. ○ farm
   ○ like
   ○ berd

6. ○ sirkel
   ○ first
   ○ under

★ ○ wirld
   ○ while
   ○ party

★ ○ heart
   ○ thirb
   ○ birthday

★ ○ child
   ○ haerd
   ○ once

165

I Game

Name _____

Place a game piece over each word your teacher says and spells. If the word appears on your card more than once, place a game piece over only one of the words. When you get five game pieces in a row, raise your hand and say, "Spelling is fun!"

Remember: Love and obey God. Nothing is more important.

J Journaling

Make a list just like Mrs. Morgan's class did in the story. Label the list:
Things I Like To Do.

A Preview

Write each word as your teacher says it.

1. _____

2. _____

3. _____

4. _____

5. _____

6. _____

7. _____

Challenge Words

8. _____   ⭐ _____

9. _____   ⭐ _____

10. _____   ⭐ _____

Scripture

"Praise the Lord ... for he has come to visit his people and has redeemed them."
Luke 1:68

B **Word Shapes**

Name _____

Write each word in the correct word shape boxes. Then, in the word shape boxes, color the letter that spells the sound of /ē/ in each word. Circle the words which have two syllables. Draw a line under the word which has three syllables.

1. any

2. baby

3. every

4. family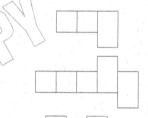

5. holy

6. only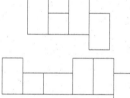

7. penny

8. ready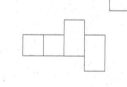

9. story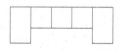

10. very

☆ **Challenge**

Draw the correctly shaped boxes around each letter in these words.

c i t y   e a s y   s t u d y

C Hide and Seek

Name _____

Circle a cookie for each word you spell correctly.

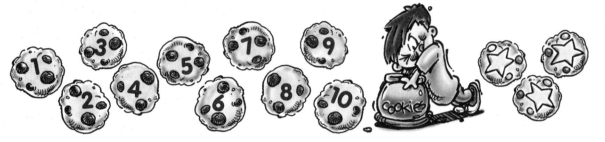

D Other Word Forms

Using the words below, follow the instructions given by your teacher.

readier   families

readiest   cities

holier   pennies

holiest   babies

easier

easiest

stories

studies

E Fun Ways to Spell

Initial the box of each activity you finish.

1.

Spell your words with markers...

3.

Spell your words with snapping...

2.

Spell your words with letter tiles...

4.

Spell your words with finger paint...

Place each set of word groups in order to write a sentence. Circle the spelling words.

all came. family Our

1. _____

story. ready We are for a

2. _____

our about God. It is holy

3. _____

only one I have penny.

4. _____

The very big. not baby is

5. _____

ice cream? any Is there

6. _____

wrapped. gift is Every

7. _____

Word Bank

any	every	holy	penny	story
baby	family	only	ready	very

G Dictation

Name _____

Listen and write the missing words.

1. _____ _____ _____ _____

   _____ _____.

2. _____ _____ brought _____ food.

3. _____ _____ ___ _____ _____ _____

   ___ party yet?

4. Daniel _____ _____.

H Proofreading

One word in each set is misspelled. Fill in the oval by the misspelled word.

1. ◯ baby
   ◯ peny
   ◯ bear

2. ◯ color
   ◯ story
   ◯ iny

3. ◯ evry
   ◯ pray
   ◯ very

4. ◯ holy
   ◯ air
   ◯ reddy

5. ◯ ownly
   ◯ water
   ◯ part

6. ◯ snow
   ◯ famly
   ◯ train

⭐ ◯ over
   ◯ ezy
   ◯ great

⭐ ◯ bath
   ◯ sity
   ◯ mowing

⭐ ◯ Jesus
   ◯ stuby
   ◯ apple

I Game

Name _____

Help Setsuko find Chimi. Color one space for each word you or your team spells correctly from this week's word list.

Remember: God loved you so much He sent Jesus to save you.

J Journaling

Finish this message to God in your journal: **Thank You for. . . I praise You because. . . When I feel lost I will. . . I know You love me because. . .**

A Test-Words

Name _____

Write each spelling word on the line as your teacher says it.

1. _____   1. _____

2. _____   2. _____

3. _____   3. _____

4. _____   4. _____

5. _____   5. _____

B Test-Sentences

The two underlined words in each of the sentences are misspelled. Write the sentences on the lines below, spelling each underlined word correctly.

Each <u>dey</u> she <u>plaez</u> with me.

1. _____

Put <u>som</u> sand in <u>thier</u> bucket.

2. _____

Let's all <u>sitt</u> in a <u>sirkle</u>.

3. _____

☆ **Test-Challenge Words**

On a sheet of paper, write each challenge word as your teacher says it.

C Test-Dictation

Listen and write the missing words.

Name _____

1. ____ ____ ____ ____ ____ ____.

2. ____ ____ ____ ____?

3. _____ __ ____ birthday.

D Test-Proofreading

One word in each set is misspelled. Fill in the oval by the misspelled word.

1. ◯ ferst
   ◯ farm
   ◯ purple

2. ◯ work
   ◯ penny
   ◯ evry

3. ◯ water
   ◯ stae
   ◯ holy

4. ◯ darck
   ◯ pay
   ◯ fine

5. ◯ card
   ◯ coler
   ◯ train

6. ◯ farr
   ◯ work
   ◯ were

7. ◯ penny
   ◯ part
   ◯ iye

8. ◯ werd
   ◯ way
   ◯ yard

9. ◯ ownli
   ◯ fire
   ◯ like

⭐ **Test-Challenge Words**

On a sheet of paper, write each challenge word as your teacher says it.

Color each bike helmet on which the word is spelled incorrectly.

⭐ **Test-Challenge Words**

On a sheet of paper, write each challenge word as your teacher says it.

Stephen got hit by a car while crossing the street on his bike. A lot of people helped Stephen when he got hurt. Use some of them as your team names for this game.

Review

Lesson
18

the emergency room doctors

the ambulance drivers

the paramedics

Remember: Even when bad things happen, God is always there.

G Test-Words

Name _____

Write each spelling word on the line as your teacher says it.

1. _____   6. _____

2. _____   7. _____

3. _____   8. _____

4. _____   9. _____

5. _____   10. _____

H Test-Sentences

The two underlined words in each of the sentences are misspelled. Write the sentences on the lines below, spelling each underlined word correctly.

Dad was <u>hapie</u> to read the <u>stori</u>.

1. _____

<u>muthir</u> has dinner <u>redy</u> for us.

2. _____

The <u>broun</u> leaf is <u>veri</u> brittle.

3. _____

☆ Test-Challenge Words

On a sheet of paper, write each challenge word as your teacher says it.

I Writing Assessment

Name _____

Make a list of all the bicycle safety rules you know. Label your list: **Bicycle Safety**. Below your list, draw a picture of a bicycle accident you had or saw happen.

1. _____

2. _____

3. _____

4. _____

5. _____

Scripture

"I am with you always, even to the end of the world." Matt. 28:20

Spelling Is Fun!

This certificate is awarded to

_____

for practicing the following words, by doing terrific spelling activities and playing great spelling games!

Date _____

paint	arm	air	bird	any
pay	barn	bear	circle	baby
plays	car	eye	color	every
pray	card	fine	first	family
rain	dark	fire	purple	holy
say	far	like	under	only
stay	farm	line	water	penny
today	hard	their	were	ready
train	part	where	word	story
way	yard	write	work	very
☆ birthday	☆ heart	☆ beside	☆ heard	☆ city
☆ praise	☆ large	☆ care	☆ third	☆ easy
☆ stayed	☆ party	☆ while	☆ world	☆ study

A Reason For Spelling®

Dear Parent,

We are about to begin a new spelling unit containing five weekly lessons. A set of ten words plus three challenge words will be studied each week. All the words will be reviewed in the sixth week.

Values based on the Scriptures listed below will be taught in each lesson.

Lesson 19	Lesson 20	Lesson 21	Lesson 22	Lesson 23
books	food	around	boys	also
could	new	bow	door	always
dear	noon	count	enjoy	children
ear	room	cow	form	draw
full	soon	found	horse	each
hear	too	house	Lord	small
here	tooth	round	noise	such
took	use	sound	orange	walk
wood	who	south	store	want
would	zoo	vowel	toy	which
☆ looked	☆ balloon	☆ cloud	☆ before	☆ called
☆ stood	☆ knew	☆ crown	☆ important	☆ lunch
☆ year	☆ through	☆ flower	☆ voice	☆ wanted
Matt. 6:34	Luke 15:10	Mark 4:23,24	Luke 11:13	Luke 11:28

Name _____

Write each word as your teacher says it.

1. _____

2. _____

3. _____

4. _____

5. _____

6. _____

7. _____

8. _____

9. _____

10. _____

Challenge Words

⭐ _____

⭐ _____

⭐ _____

Scripture

"God will take care of your tomorrow... Live one day at a time."
Matt. 6:34

Name _____

Write each word in the correct word shape boxes. Then, in the word shape boxes, color the letter or letters that spell the sound of /îr/ or /u̇/ in each word. Circle the words in which /u̇/ is spelled with **ou**.

1. books

2. could

3. dear

4. ear

5. full

6. hear

7. here

8. took

9. wood

10. would

☆ **Challenge**

Draw the correctly shaped boxes around each letter in these words.

looked   stood   year

C Hide and Seek

Name _____

Circle a cookie for each word you spell correctly.

D Other Word Forms

Using the words below, follow the instructions given by your teacher.

book	fuller
booked	hears
booking	look
dears	looks
dearest	looking
dearly	wooden
ears	years
fullest	

E Fun Ways to Spell

Initial the box of each activity you finish.

1. ☐

Spell your words with crayon…

3. ☐

Spell your words with rhythm instruments…

2. ☐

Spell your words with stencils…

4. ☐

Spell your words with cotton balls...

183

Write each set of spelling words in alphabetical order.

1. would _____

full _____

ear _____

took _____

2. dear _____

books _____

could _____

here _____

3. took _____

wood _____

hear _____

dear _____

☆ stood _____

year _____

looked _____

lamp _____

A B C D E F G H I J K L M N O P Q R S T U V W X Y Z

a b c d e f g h i j k l m n o p q r s t u v w x y z

Words with /îr/ or /u̇/

Lesson

19

G Dictation

Name _____

Listen and write the missing words.

1. Rosa's basket _____ ____ ___ _____.

2. _____ ____ ___ ___ calling?

3. _____ ___ ___ ___ ___ ___need.

4. Who ____ my ___ muffs?

H Proofreading

One word in each set is misspelled. Fill in the oval by the misspelled word.

1. ○ ready
   ○ could
   ○ daer

2. ○ ful
   ○ throw
   ○ family

3. ○ work
   ○ woob
   ○ books

4. ○ into
   ○ heer
   ○ arm

5. ○ took
   ○ penny
   ○ woud

6. ○ eer
   ○ here
   ○ fire

⭐ ○ third
   ○ stoob
   ○ while

⭐ ○ city
   ○ lookt
   ○ study

⭐ ○ yeer
   ○ care
   ○ world

I **Game**

Name _____

Sign Stephen's cast. Each time a person on your team spells a word correctly from this week's word list, write their name on Stephen's cast.

Remember: Only God is big enough to take care of tomorrow. Choose not
to worry.

J **Journaling**

At the top of your journal page, write: **Things I Worry About**. Make a
list of at least three things that worry you. At the bottom of the page,
write: **God will take care of my tomorrow.**

A Preview

Write each word as your teacher says it.

Name _____

1. _____

2. _____

3. _____

4. _____

5. _____

6. _____

7. _____

8. _____

9. _____

10. _____

Challenge Words

 _____

_____

_____

Scripture

"There is joy in the presence of the angels of God when one sinner repents."
Luke 15:10

Write each word in the correct word shape boxes. Then, in the word shape boxes, color the letter or letters that spell the sound of /ü/ or /ū/ in each word. Circle the word which has the sound of /ū/.

1. food

2. new

3. noon

4. room

5. soon

6. too

7. tooth

8. use

9. who

10. zoo

☆ **Challenge**

Draw the correctly shaped boxes around each letter in these words.

balloon   knew   through

C Hide and Seek

Name _____

Circle a cookie for each word you spell correctly.

D Other Word Forms

Using the words below, follow the instructions given by your teacher.

balloons	roomiest
foods	sooner
news	soonest
newer	used
newest	who's
rooms	zoos
roomy	
roomier	

EXAMINATION COPY

E Fun Ways to Spell

 Initial the box of each activity you finish.

1.

Spell your words with an eraser…

3.

Spell your words with clapping…

2.

Spell your words with paint...

4.

Spell your words in wet sand…

Name _____

Use the clues to write the spelling words.

1. Place animals live: _____

2. Something to eat: _____

3. Middle of the day: _____

4. _____ lost twenty dollars?

5. Not a long time: _____

6. I have a _____ pad of paper.

7. You may not _____ my pad of paper!

8. He stared out the window of his _____.

9. Your front one may have fallen out: _____

10. You can choose to repent, _____.

⭐ Christopher _____ he should not yell at Cori.

⭐ Something you can pop: _____

⭐ Christopher was _____ with his job at school.

Word Bank

food	noon	soon	tooth	who	⭐ balloon	⭐ through
new	room	too	use	zoo	⭐ knew	

G Dictation

Name _____

Listen and write the missing words.

1. _____ ___ _____ ___ _____ _____

    ___ _____.

2. _____ _____ _____ ___ _____ ___

    ___ _____.

3. _____ _____ _____ _____ _____ camera?

4. _____ ____ lose ____ _____, ___?

H Proofreading

One word in each set is misspelled. Fill in the oval by the misspelled word.

1. ⬭ noon
   ⬭ story
   ⬭ tooht

2. ⬭ ear
   ⬭ room
   ⬭ foob

3. ⬭ very
   ⬭ too
   ⬭ nuw

4. ⬭ only
   ⬭ zu
   ⬭ baby

5. ⬭ hoo
   ⬭ wood
   ⬭ soon

6. ⬭ uze
   ⬭ fine
   ⬭ far

★ ⬭ stood
   ⬭ third
   ⬭ thru

★ ⬭ baloon
   ⬭ easy
   ⬭ job

★ ⬭ because
   ⬭ sentence
   ⬭ knuw

191

I | Game

Name _____

Christopher wants to return the money he found. Lead the way to the school office by moving one space each time you or your team spells a word correctly from this week's word list.

Remember: The angels sing for joy when you ask God's forgiveness.

J | Journaling

In your journal, write about something you did that was wrong. What did you do? How did you feel? How do you think the angels felt when you made your mistake right?

A Preview

Write each word as your teacher says it.

Name _____

1. _____

2. _____

3. _____

4. _____

5. _____

6. _____

7. _____

Challenge Words

8. _____ ☆ _____

9. _____ ☆ _____

10. _____ ☆ _____

Scripture

"If you have ears, listen! And be sure to put into practice what you hear."
Mark 4:23,24

Name _____

Write each word in the correct word shape boxes. Then, in the word shape boxes, color the letters that spell the diphthong **/ou/** in each word. Circle the words in which the diphthong **/ou/** is spelled with **ow**.

Words with /ou/

Lesson **21**

1. around
2. bow
3. count
4. cow
5. found
6. house
7. round
8. sound
9. south
10. vowel

⭐ **Challenge**

Draw the correctly shaped boxes around each letter in these words.

cloud   crown   flower

C Hide and Seek

Name _____

Circle a cookie for each word you spell correctly.

D Other Word Forms

Using the words below, follow the instructions given by your teacher.

bows	flowers	rounding
bowed	flowered	sounds
cloudy	flowering	sounded
counts	houses	sounding
counted	housed	vowels
counting	housing	
cows	rounder	
crown	roundest	

E Fun Ways to Spell

Initial the box of each activity you finish.

1. ☐

Spell your words with puzzles…

3. ☐

Spell your words out loud…

2. ☐

Spell your words on a paper chain …

4. ☐

Spell your words with split peas...

Write the spelling word to complete each sentence.

1. The softball is _____.

2. It is warmer in the _____.

3. We learned what the _____ "o" says with "w".

4. There was a pleading _____ in Matthew's voice.

5. Alex _____ his glove at the taco place.

6. Go back in the _____ and get your jacket.

7. Don't _____ on winning every T-Ball game.

8. The boys stood _____ their coach.

9. The _____ stood in the field and ate grass.

10. Take a _____ after that fine catch.

☆ The _____ covered the sun.

☆ You will have stars in your _____.

☆ One _____ was blooming in the garden.

Word Bank						
around	count	found	round	south	☆ cloud	☆ flower
bow	cow	house	sound	vowel	☆ crown	

196

G Dictation

Name _____

Listen and write the missing words.

1. _____ _____ walked _____

_____ _____.

2. _____ _____ birds flying _____.

3. _____ _____ needs ___ least

_____ _____.

4. Stephen _____ dish.

H Proofreading

One word in each set is misspelled. Fill in the oval by the misspelled word.

1. ◯ yard
   ◯ zoo
   ◯ fownd

2. ◯ vowel
   ◯ arownd
   ◯ food

3. ◯ souht
   ◯ cow
   ◯ could

4. ◯ under
   ◯ cownt
   ◯ new

5. ◯ sounb
   ◯ ear
   ◯ round

6. ◯ hows
   ◯ bow
   ◯ here

 ◯ balloon
   ◯ croun
   ◯ stood

⭐ ◯ through
   ◯ clowd
   ◯ stayed

⭐ ◯ flowr
   ◯ knew
   ◯ looked

I | Game

Matthew and Alex each forgot something. Run home to find what they left behind. Color one space each time you or your team spells a word correctly from this week's word list.

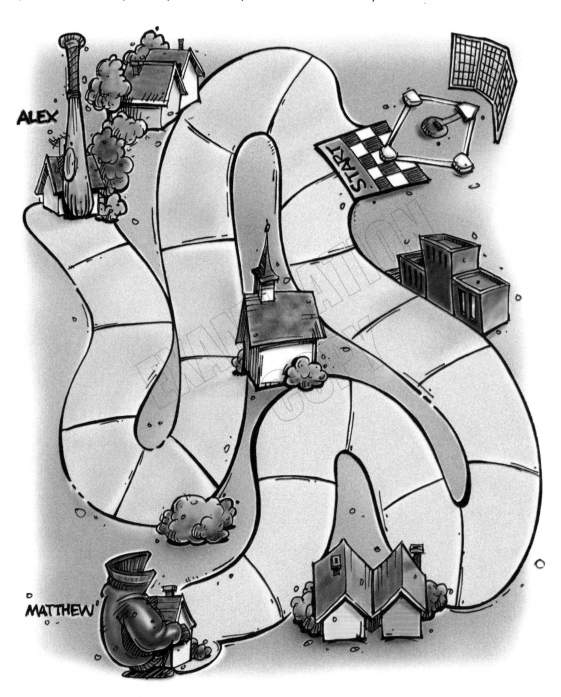

Remember: Listen carefully to what you are told to do and then do it carefully.

J | Journaling

Design a sign in your journal telling kids to listen and do what they are told.

A Preview

Write each word as your teacher says it.

Name _____

1. _____

2. _____

3. _____

4. _____

5. _____

6. _____

7. _____

8. _____

9. _____

10. _____

Challenge Words

⭐ _____

⭐ _____

⭐ _____

Scripture

"Your heavenly Father will ... give the Holy Spirit to those who ask for him."
Luke 11:13

Write each word in the correct word shape boxes. Then, in the word shape boxes, color the letters that spell the sound of /ôr/ or the diphthong /oi/ in each word. Circle the word in which /ôr/ is spelled with **oor**.

1. boys

2. door

3. enjoy

4. form

5. horse

6. Lord

7. noise

8. orange

9. store

10. toy

☆ **Challenge**

Draw the correctly shaped boxes around each letter in these words.

before   important   voice

C Hide and Seek

Circle a cookie for each word you spell correctly.

D Other Word Forms

Using the words below, follow the instructions given by your teacher.

boy	horses	stored	voicing
doors	horsed	storing	
enjoys	horsing	toys	
enjoyed	Lords	toyed	
enjoying	noises	toying	
forms	noisy	unimportant	
formed	oranges	voices	
forming	stores	voiced	

E Fun Ways to Spell

Initial the box of each activity you finish.

1.

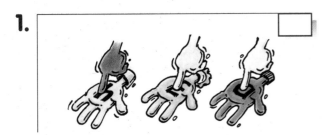

Spell your words in your classmate's hand...

3.

Spell your words out of the letter box...

2.

Spell your words with paper cups...

4.

Spell your words with shaving cream...

201

F Crossword

Name _____

Use the puzzle clues to write the spelling words.

Across

3. open the _____
5. color
8. something to play with
9. to like
10 a place to buy things

Down

1. to shape
2. animal
4. God
6. loud sound
7. not girls but _____

Word Bank

boys	enjoy	horse	noise	store
door	form	Lord	orange	toy

G Dictation

Name _____

Listen **and** write the missing words.

1. _____ _____ _____ ___ ___ airplane.

2. Daniel led _____ _____ through _____
   _____ _____.

3. ___ ___ ___ ___ ___ ___
   ___ ___.

4. _____ _____ loves _____ ___ ___.

H Proofreading

One word in each set is misspelled. Fill in the oval by the misspelled word.

1. ○ Lord
   ○ dear
   ○ engoy

2. ○ hors
   ○ took
   ○ toy

3. ○ first
   ○ boyz
   ○ where

4. ○ noon
   ○ store
   ○ dor

5. ○ circle
   ○ line
   ○ noiz

6. ○ ornge
   ○ baby
   ○ form

⭐ ○ flower
   ○ importnt
   ○ stood

⭐ ○ crown
   ○ befour
   ○ through

⭐ ○ easy
   ○ vois
   ○ year

I | **Game**

Name _____

Place a game piece over each word your teacher says and spells. If the word appears on your card more than once, place a game piece over only one of the words. When you get five game pieces in a row, raise your hand and say, "Spelling is fun!"

Remember: God gives us the Holy Spirit to guide us, but we must choose to listen to Him.

J | **Journaling**

In your journal, write about a time that you didn't know the right thing to do. Finish this sentence in your journal: **When I don't know what I should do, I will. . .**

A | Preview

Write each word as your teacher says it.

Name _____

1. _____

2. _____

3. _____

4. _____

5. _____

6. _____

7. _____

8. _____

9. _____

10. _____

Challenge Words

☆ _____

☆ _____

☆ _____

Scripture

"Blessed are all who hear the Word of God and put it into practice." Luke 11:28

Write each word in the correct word shape boxes. Then, in the word shape boxes, color the letter or letters that spell the sound of /ô/ or /ch/ in each word. Circle the word which has two digraphs.

1. also

2. always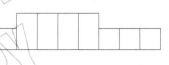

3. children

4. draw

5. each

6. small

7. such

8. walk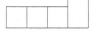

9. want

10. which

☆ **Challenge**

Draw the correctly shaped boxes around each letter in these words.

called   lunch   wanted

C Hide and Seek

Circle a cookie for each word you spell correctly.

Name

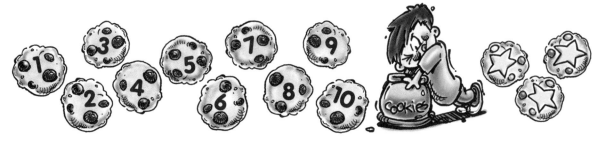

D Other Word Forms

Using the words below, follow the instructions given by your teacher.

smaller   lunches

smallest   call

draws   calling

walks

walked

walking

wants

wanting

E Fun Ways to Spell

Initial the box of each activity you finish.

1.

Spell your words with markers...

3.

Spell your words with snapping...

2.

Spell your words with letter tiles...

4.

Spell your words with finger paint...

F **Unscramble Words**

Name _____

Use the underlined letters to write a spelling word.

1. _____ The lirdench made origami bunnies.

2. _____ They made hace one by folding paper.

3. _____ Setsuko laso made some baby bunnies.

4. _____ The baby bunnies were very mlasl.

5. _____ Can you wrad a picture of a bunny?

6. _____ We tanw to be kind to others.

7. _____ Some older people find it hard to lakw.

8. _____ Visiting them is hsuc a nice thing to do.

9. _____ Helping others is slawya a good choice.

10. _____ Wchih bunny do you like the best?

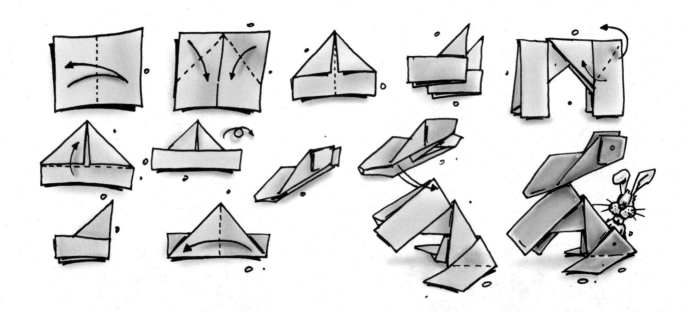

Word Bank

also	children	each	such	want
always	draw	small	walk	which

G Dictation

Name _____

Listen and write the missing words.

1. _____ _____ _____ _____

   _____ _____?

2. Sarah _____ brings ____ doll.

3. Those _____ _____ _____ apples.

4. _____ ____ _____

   ___ _____?

H Proofreading

One word in each set is misspelled. Fill in the oval by the misspelled word.

1. ○ allwayz
   ○ left
   ○ none

2. ○ smal
   ○ want
   ○ who

3. ○ could
   ○ wich
   ○ such

4. ○ noon
   ○ draw
   ○ allso

5. ○ water
   ○ paint
   ○ wak

6. ○ children
   ○ quit
   ○ eech

☆ ○ caled
   ○ looked
   ○ praise

☆ ○ party
   ○ luch
   ○ world

☆ ○ wonted
   ○ balloon
   ○ knew

I Game

Name _____

Follow the rabbit tracks to Pleasant Valley Retirement Center. Move one space each time you or your team spells a word correctly from this week's word list.

Remember: God sends special blessings to those who listen to and obey His Word.

J Journaling

Make a list in your journal of people you know who might be lonely. Label your list: **People to Cheer Up**.

A Test-Words

Name _____

Write each spelling word on the line as your teacher says it.

1. _____   1. _____

2. _____   2. _____

3. _____   3. _____

4. _____   4. _____

5. _____   5. _____

B Test-Sentences

The two underlined words in each of the sentences are misspelled. Write the sentences on the lines below, spelling each underlined word correctly.

The <u>gerl</u> will <u>cownt</u> the money.

1. _____

The <u>blak</u> dog made a lot of <u>noiz</u>.

2. _____

In <u>touwn</u> there is a bigger <u>stor</u>.

3. _____

⭐ **Test-Challenge Words**

On a sheet of paper, write each challenge word as your teacher says it.

C **Test-Dictation**

Name _____

Listen and write the missing words.

1. _____ ___ _____ rain _____?

2. _____ soccer _____ ___ _____.

3. ____ _____ _____ ____ music?

D **Test-Proofreading**

One word in each set is misspelled. Fill in the oval by the misspelled word.

1. ◯ dor
   ◯ ear
   ◯ noon

2. ◯ around
   ◯ Lorb
   ◯ toy

3. ◯ roum
   ◯ small
   ◯ would

4. ◯ who
   ◯ house
   ◯ kow

5. ◯ boyz
   ◯ walk
   ◯ children

6. ◯ here
   ◯ cood
   ◯ soon

7. ◯ bow
   ◯ nyu
   ◯ enjoy

8. ◯ draw
   ◯ wood
   ◯ sowth

9. ◯ sutch
   ◯ zoo
   ◯ sound

☆ **Test-Challenge Words**

On a sheet of paper, write each challenge word as your teacher says it.

E Test-Shapes

Name ______________________________

Color each marker on which the word is spelled incorrectly.

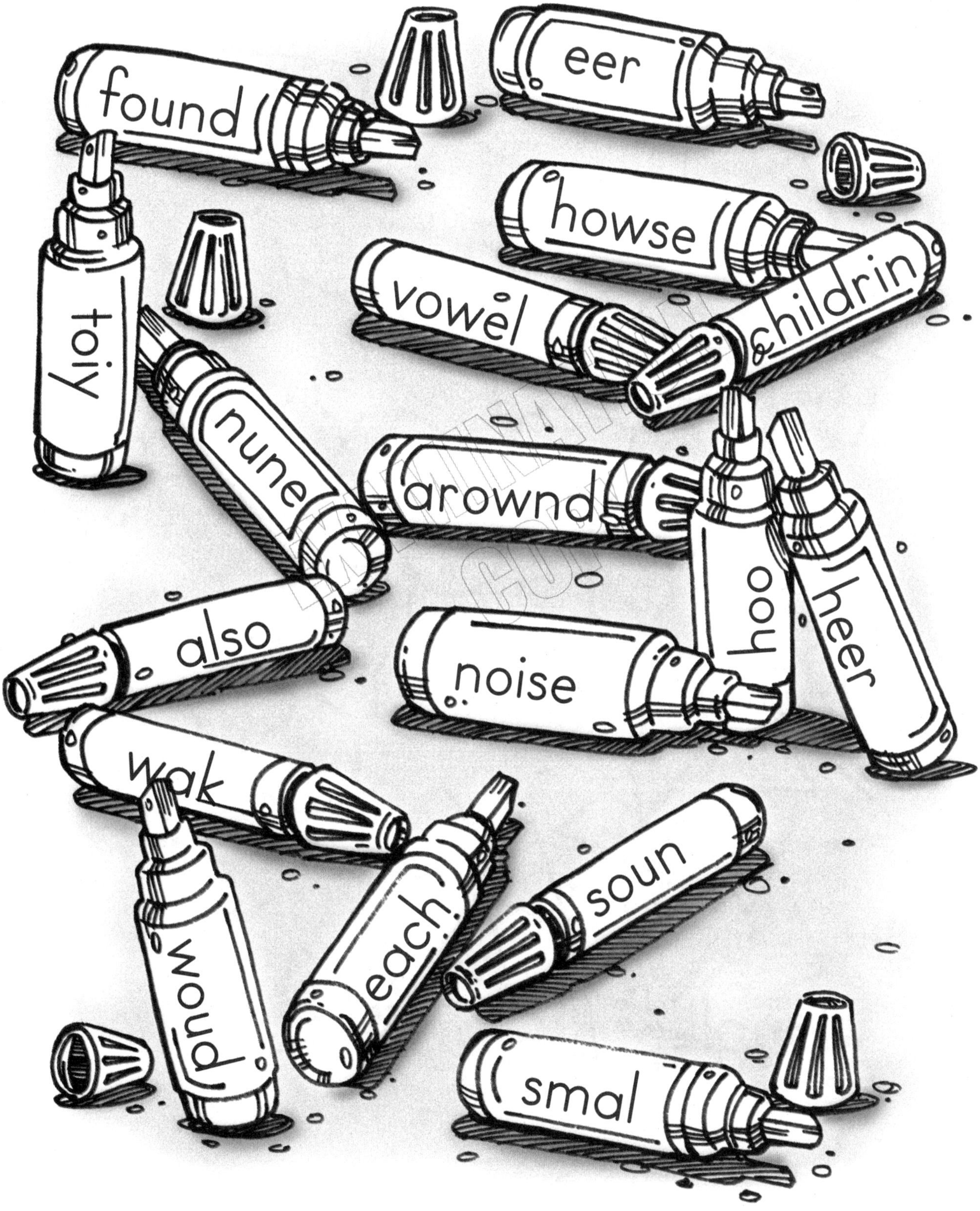
found
eer
howse
vowel
childrin
toiy
nune
arownd
hoo
heer
also
noise
wak
soun
woud
each
smal

Test-Challenge Words

On a sheet of paper, write each challenge word as your teacher says it.

Name _____

Kristin shared her markers with Katelynn when their class was completing a worksheet on geometric shapes. Use shapes as your team names for this game. Place a sticker each time you or your team spells a review word correctly.

Remember: Treat others the way you want to be treated.

G Test-Words

Name _____

Write each spelling word on the line as your teacher says it.

1. _____   6. _____

2. _____   7. _____

3. _____   8. _____

4. _____   9. _____

5. _____   10. _____

H Test-Sentences

The two underlined words in each of the sentences are misspelled. Write the sentences on the lines below, spelling each underlined word correctly.

My <u>muther</u> said we could ride the <u>hors</u>.

1. _____

<u>may</u> I keep this <u>touth</u> I pulled ?

2. _____

All the <u>litle</u> beads are <u>rownd</u>.

3. _____

☆ **Test-Challenge Words**

On a sheet of paper, write each challenge word as your teacher says it.

I Writing Assessment

Write at least four
sentences about a time
when you helped someone.

Name _____

1. _____

_____

2. _____

_____

3. _____

_____

4. _____

_____

Scripture

"Do for others what you want them to do for you." Matt. 7:12

Spelling Is Fun!

EXAMINATION COPY

A Reason For SPELLING

This certificate is awarded to

_____

for practicing the following words, by doing terrific spelling activities and playing great spelling games!

Date _____

books	food	around	boys	also
could	new	bow	door	always
dear	noon	count	enjoy	children
ear	room	cow	form	draw
full	soon	found	horse	each
hear	too	house	Lord	small
here	tooth	round	noise	such
took	use	sound	orange	walk
wood	who	south	store	want
would	zoo	vowel	toy	which
☆ looked	☆ balloon	☆ cloud	☆ before	☆ called
☆ stood	☆ knew	☆ crown	☆ important	☆ lunch
☆ year	☆ through	☆ flower	☆ voice	☆ wanted

A Reason For Spelling

Dear Parent,

    We are about to begin the last spelling unit of the year containing five weekly lessons. A set of ten words plus three challenge words will be studied each week. All the words will be reviewed in the sixth week.

    Values based on the Scriptures listed below will be taught in each lesson.

Lesson 25	Lesson 26	Lesson 27	Lesson 28	Lesson 29
dish	band	back	another	bell
finish	bend	bring	both	better
fish	blind	clock	other	dress
shoe	candy	duck	thank	funny
shop	end	hang	these	grass
should	find	milk	thick	guess
show	grand	sick	thin	mitten
shut	Indian	sing	think	pull
wash	kind	talk	those	rabbit
wish	pond	truck	thought	still
☆ shelf	☆ friend	☆ along	☆ brother	☆ different
☆ shoes	☆ index	☆ block	☆ father	☆ dinner
☆ short	☆ second	☆ something	☆ together	☆ letter
Luke 4:19	John 8:32	Matt. 5:47	Matt. 4:17	Luke 12:37

A **Preview**

Write each word as your teacher says it.

Name _____

1. _____

2. _____

3. _____

4. _____

5. _____

6. _____

7. _____

8. _____

9. _____

10. _____

Challenge Words

⭐ _____

⭐ _____

⭐ _____

Words with /sh/

Lesson
25

Scripture

"God is ready to give blessings to all who come to him." Luke 4:19

Write each word in the correct word shape boxes. Then, in the word shape boxes, color the letters that spell the sound of /**sh**/ in each word. Circle the words that end with the digraph **sh**.

1. dish

2. finish

3. fish

4. shoe

5. shop

6. should

7. show

8. shut

9. wash

10. wish

☆ **Challenge**

Draw the correctly shaped boxes around each letter in these words.

s h e l f   s h o e s   s h o r t

C Hide and Seek

Name _____

Circle a cookie for each word you spell correctly.

D Other Word Forms

Using the words below, follow the instructions given by your teacher.

dishes	shoe	showing	wishing
dished	shoes	shuts	
finishes	shopped	shutting	
finished	shopping	washes	
finishing	shorter	washed	
fished	shortest	washing	
fishing	shows	wishes	
ships	showed	wished	

E Fun Ways to Spell

Initial the box of each activity you finish.

1. ☐

Spell your words with crayon…

3. ☐

Spell your words with rhythm instruments…

2. ☐

Spell your words with sidewalk chalk…

4. ☐

Spell your words with cotton balls...

F **Letter Change**

Name _____

Help Stephen with his homework. Change the underlined letter or letters and write the spelling word on the blank.

1. _____ The d<u>a</u>sh was full of potatoes.

2. _____ The gold fis<u>t</u> swam to the top.

3. _____ I w<u>a</u>sh I could play T-ball.

4. _____ Your sho<u>d</u> string is untied.

5. _____ This sh<u>i</u>p sells tapes and books.

6. _____ We <u>w</u>ould thank God.

7. _____ Matthew will s<u>l</u>ow me how.

8. _____ The back door is sh<u>o</u>t.

9. _____ We w<u>i</u>sh our hands.

10. _____ Let's f<u>am</u>ish the game now.

Word Bank

dish	fish	shop	show	wash
finish	shoe	should	shut	wish

G Dictation

Name _____

Listen and write the missing words.

1. _____ __ _____ ____ window?

2. Tony _____ _____ ____ __ gift.

3. Please _____ ____ __ ___ _____

___ ____.

4. _____ polishing _____.

H Proofreading

One word in each set is misspelled. Fill in the oval by the misspelled word.

1. ◯ air
   ◯ shood
   ◯ shut

2. ◯ dark
   ◯ pay
   ◯ wosh

3. ◯ shopp
   ◯ form
   ◯ dish

4. ◯ ready
   ◯ wish
   ◯ shooe

5. ◯ bear
   ◯ tooth
   ◯ sho

6. ◯ finsh
   ◯ fish
   ◯ children

☆ ◯ heart
  ◯ shefl
  ◯ lunch

☆ ◯ shotr
  ◯ voice
  ◯ large

☆ ◯ important
  ◯ flower
  ◯ shooz

I Game

Name _____

Run the bases in a game of T-ball while Stephen referees. Move one space each time you or your team spells a word correctly from this week's word list.

Remember: Call out to God and ask Him for His blessing.

J Journaling

Write a thank-you letter in your journal to someone who has been a blessing to you.

A Preview

Write each word as your teacher says it.

Name _____

1. _____

2. _____

3. _____

4. _____

5. _____

6. _____

7. _____

8. _____

9. _____

10. _____

Challenge Words

⭐ _____

⭐ _____

⭐ _____

Scripture

"You will know the truth, and the truth will set you free." John 8:32

Name _____

Write each word in the correct word shape boxes. Then, in the word shape boxes, color the letters that spell the sound of **nd** in each word. Circle the words in which **nd** comes in the middle of the word.

1. band

2. bend

3. blind

4. candy

5. end

6. find

7. grand

8. Indian

9. kind

10. pond

☆ **Challenge**

Draw the correctly shaped boxes around each letter in these words.

friend   index   second

C Hide and Seek

Name _____

Circle a cookie for each word you spell correctly.

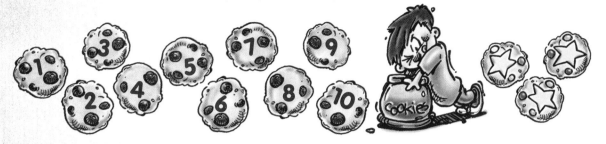

D Other Word Forms

Using the words below, follow the instructions given by your teacher.

bands	ending	seconded
banded	finds	
bends	friends	
bending	indexes	
blinded	Indians	
blinding	kinds	
candies	ponds	
ended	seconds	

E Fun Ways to Spell

Initial the box of each activity you finish.

1. □

Spell your words with an eraser…

3. □

Spell your words with clapping…

2. □

Spell your words with paint...

4. □

Spell your words in wet sand…

Name _____

These word pairs are guide words like those that appear in a dictionary. Write your spelling words on the lines below the set of guide words for the page on which each spelling word would appear. Use words from the Word Bank below.

ball – big

_____

_____

black – dog

_____

far – green

_____

_____

ear – every

_____

ice cream – itch

_____

keep – know

_____

pick – race

_____

Word Bank

band	blind	end	grand	kind
bend	candy	find	Indian	pond

G Dictation

Name _____

Listen and write the missing words.

1. ___ ___ _____ ___ watch ___

   marching _____.

2. Taffy ___ _____ ___ ___ _____.

3. _____ ___ ___ _____ _____

   _____ _____.

4. _____ _____.

H Proofreading

One word in each set is misspelled. Fill in the oval by the misspelled word.

1. ○ been
   ○ candi
   ○ grand

2. ○ podn
   ○ soft
   ○ find

3. ○ dand
   ○ show
   ○ plan

4. ○ end
   ○ sister
   ○ blinde

5. ○ wash
   ○ biend
   ○ kind

6. ○ must
   ○ indian
   ○ shoe

 ○ frend
   ○ through
   ○ shoes

 ○ crown
   ○ shelf
   ○ endex

 ○ secund
   ○ beside
   ○ short

I | Game

Name _____

Tony is getting treated to ice cream after his baseball game. Lead the way to the ice cream shop by moving one space each time you or your team spells a word correctly from this week's word list.

Remember: God does not want you to feel guilty for the sins of others.

J | Journaling

In your journal, make a list of people whom you love.
Label the list: **People I Love**.

A Preview

Write each word as your teacher says it.

Name _____

1. _____

2. _____

3. _____

4. _____

5. _____

6. _____

7. _____

8. _____

9. _____

10. _____

Challenge Words

☆ _____

☆ _____

☆ _____

Scripture

"If you are friendly only to your friends, how are you different from anyone else?" Matt. 5:47

B **Word Shapes**

Name _____

Write each word in the correct word shape boxes. Then, in the word shape boxes, color the letter or letters that spell the sound of **/ng/** or **/k/** in each word. Circle the word which has a silent **l**.

1. back

2. bring

3. clock

4. duck

5. hang

6. milk

7. sick

8. sing

9. talk

10. truck

☆ **Challenge**

Draw the correctly shaped boxes around each letter in these words.

a l o n g   b l o c k   s o m e t h i n g

C Hide and Seek

Circle a cookie for each word you spell correctly.

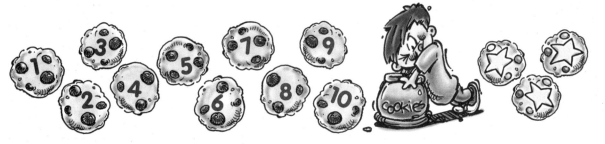

D Other Word Forms

Using the words below, follow the instructions given by your teacher.

backs	brought	hangs	sickest	talking
backed	bringing	hung	sickly	talker
backing	clocks	hanging	sings	trucks
backer	clocked	hanger	sang	trucked
blocks	clocking	milks	singing	trucking
blocked	ducks	milked	singer	trucker
blocking	ducked	milking	talks	
brings	ducking	sicker	talked	

E Fun Ways to Spell

Initial the box of each activity you finish.

1.

Spell your words with puzzles…

2.

Spell your words on a paper chain …

3.

Spell your words out loud…

4.

Spell your words with split peas...

F **Word Change**

Name _____

Write spelling words in place of the underlined words.

1. Setsuko likes to <u>say words</u> to her cousins. _____

2. They will <u>fasten</u> a banner on the wall. _____

3. Everyone will <u>carry in</u> birthday presents. _____

4. Father will come through the <u>not in front</u> door.

   _____

5. The <u>thing that tells time</u> just struck six o'clock.

   _____

6. I think I hear his <u>bigger than a car</u> coming now.

   _____

7. <u>Bend down</u> behind the couch to surprise him!

   _____

8. We'll <u>make music with voices</u> "Happy Birthday to You". _____

9. Do you want a glass of <u>white drink from a cow</u> with your cake? _____

Word Bank				
back	clock	hang	sick	talk
bring	duck	milk	sing	truck

234

G Dictation

Name _____

Listen and write the missing words.

1. _____ _____ _____ _____ drives _____

_____ _____.

2. _____ _____ preened _____ feathers

_____ _____ _____.

3. _____ _____ _____ _____ _____

_____ wall.

Lesson
27

H Proofreading

One word in each set is misspelled. Fill in the oval by the misspelled word.

1. ⬭ finish
   ⬭ truck
   ⬭ sinj

2. ⬭ hayg
   ⬭ shop
   ⬭ purple

3. ⬭ clok
   ⬭ car
   ⬭ milk

4. ⬭ plays
   ⬭ sik
   ⬭ its

5. ⬭ nest
   ⬭ tok
   ⬭ bring

6. ⬭ gone
   ⬭ duck
   ⬭ dack

⭐ ⬭ lunch
   ⬭ friend
   ⬭ alonj

⭐ ⬭ sumthing
   ⬭ second
   ⬭ cloud

⭐ ⬭ knew
   ⬭ blok
   ⬭ index

I | Game

Name _____

Setsuko and her mother picked up the rolls of paper towels for the woman who said unkind things about them. You help too by coloring one roll each time you or your team spells a word correctly from this week's word list.

Remember: Be kind—even to those who do not like you.

J | Journaling

Draw a picture in your journal of Jesus and you together. Underneath the picture write how you will show your love for God.

A Preview

Write each word as your teacher says it.

1. _____

2. _____

3. _____

4. _____

5. _____

6. _____

7. _____

Challenge Words

8. _____

9. _____

10. _____

⭐ _____

⭐ _____

⭐ _____

Scripture

"Turn from sin, and turn to God, for the Kingdom of heaven is near." Matt. 4:17

Name _____

Write each word in the correct word shape boxes. Then, in the word shape boxes, color the letters that spell the sound of **/th/** or **/th/** in each word.

1. another

2. both

3. other

4. thank

5. these

6. thick

7. thin

8. think

9. those

10. thought

⭐ **Challenge**

Draw the correctly shaped boxes around each letter in these words.

brother   father   together

Words with /th/ or /th/

Lesson
28

C Hide and Seek

Name _____

Circle a cookie for each word you spell correctly.

D Other Word Forms

Using the words below, follow the instructions given by your teacher.

brothers   thinner

brotherly   thinnest

fathers   thinly

others   thoughts

thanks

thicker

thickest

thickly

E Fun Ways to Spell

Initial the box of each activity you finish.

1.
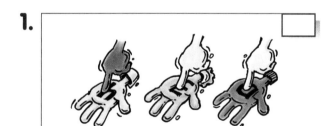
Spell your words in your classmate's hand...

3.

Spell your words out of the letter box...

2.

Spell your words with paper cups...

4.

Spell your words with shaving cream...

239

Write the spelling words that rhyme with the words in the list.

1. win, _____

2. mother, _____ _____

   ⭐ _____

3. hose, _____

4. bank, _____

5. stick, _____

6. fought, _____

7. sink, _____

8. growth, _____

9. cheese, _____

   ⭐ bother, _____

   ⭐ weather, _____

Word Bank

another	other	these	thin	those	⭐ brother	⭐ together
both	thank	thick	think	thought	⭐ father	

G Dictation

Name _____

Listen and write the missing words.

1. _____ ____ ____ ____

    _____ blankets.

2. Setsuko _____ _____ dresses

    _____ pretty.

3. ____ _____ ____ cookie.

4. __ ____ _____ ____ __ ___.

H Proofreading

One word in each set is misspelled. Fill in the oval by the misspelled word.

1. ○ candy
   ○ theez
   ○ clock

2. ○ anuther
   ○ Indian
   ○ thank

3. ○ sick
   ○ fish
   ○ thoze

4. ○ thick
   ○ thout
   ○ blind

5. ○ back
   ○ uther
   ○ thin

6. ○ bothe
   ○ should
   ○ think

☆ ○ something
   ○ bruther
   ○ block

☆ ○ fother
   ○ obey
   ○ along

☆ ○ don't
   ○ togethr
   ○ second

241

I | Game

Place a game piece over each word your teacher says and spells. If the word appears on your card more than once, place a game piece over only one of the words. When you get five game pieces in a row, raise your hand and say, "Spelling is fun!"

Remember: Turn from your own way and go God's way.

J | Journaling

Make a list in your journal of things you should "turn from" or quit doing. At the bottom of your list, write a note to Jesus asking Him to help you.

A Preview

Write each word as your teacher says it.

Name _____

1. _____

2. _____

3. _____

4. _____

5. _____

6. _____

7. _____

Challenge Words

8. _____   ⭐ _____

9. _____   ⭐ _____

10. _____   ⭐ _____

Scripture

"There will be great joy for those who are ready and waiting for his return."
Luke 12:37

Name _____

Write each word in the correct word shape boxes. Then, in the word shape boxes, color the double consonants in each word. Circle the words that have two syllables.

1. bell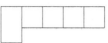

2. better

3. dress

4. funny

5. grass

6. guess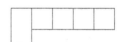

7. mitten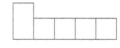

8. pull

9. rabbit

10. still

☆ **Challenge**

Draw the correctly shaped boxes around each letter in these words.

different   dinner   letter

C Hide and Seek

Circle a cookie for each word you spell correctly.

Name _____

D Other Word Forms

Using the words below, follow the instructions given by your teacher.

bells	funniest	pulls
best	grasses	pulled
dinners	guesses	pulling
dresses	guessed	rabbits
dressed	guessing	stiller
dressing	indifferent	stillest
undress	letters	
funnier	mittens	

E Fun Ways to Spell

Initial the box of each activity you finish.

1.

Spell your words with markers...

3.

Spell your words with snapping...

2.

Spell your words with letter tiles...

4.

Spell your words with finger paint...

F **Sentence Order**

Name _____

Place each set of word groups in order to write a sentence. Circle the spelling words.

looked 🖼 Dad 🖼 in ribbons. 🖼 funny

1. _____

rope to 🖼 the bell. 🖼 ring 🖼 Pull the

2. _____

the mitten 🖼 I guess 🖼 is lost.

3. _____

grass. 🖼 eats 🖼 The rabbit 🖼 fresh

4. _____

had better 🖼 this dress. 🖼 Rosa 🖼 wear

5. _____

and proud. 🖼 stood still 🖼 The buck

6. _____

Word Bank

bell	dress	grass	mitten	rabbit
better	funny	guess	pull	still

G **Dictation**

Name _____

Listen and write the missing words.

1. _____ _____ _____ ate _____ _____.

2. ____ _____ ____ _____ _____ _____

_____ wagon.

3. _____ _____ _____ _____ _____.

4. _____ _____ _____ _____ _____

_____ ____.

H **Proofreading**

One word in each set is misspelled. Fill in the oval by the misspelled word.

1. ◯ another
   ◯ grass
   ◯ beter

2. ◯ kind
   ◯ these
   ◯ dres

3. ◯ funy
   ◯ bell
   ◯ shop

4. ◯ those
   ◯ gess
   ◯ dish

5. ◯ hang
   ◯ rabit
   ◯ dress

6. ◯ end
   ◯ pull
   ◯ stil

 ◯ difrent
   ◯ balloon
   ◯ together

⭐ ◯ father
   ◯ wanted
   ◯ leter

⭐ ◯ brother
   ◯ shelf
   ◯ dinnr

I | Game

Name _____

Rosa is getting ready to visit her uncle and aunt on their farm. Help her pack by moving one space each time you or your team spells a word correctly from this week's word list.

Remember: Jesus has great plans for you!

J | Journaling

Write several sentences in your journal about a time you went somewhere special that you really enjoyed. Remember, being with your Heavenly Father will be very special!

A Test-Words

Name _____

Write each spelling word on the line as your teacher says it.

1. _____   1. _____

2. _____   2. _____

3. _____   3. _____

4. _____   4. _____

5. _____   5. _____

B Test-Sentences

The two underlined words in each of the sentences are misspelled. Write the sentences on the lines below, spelling each underlined word correctly.

Sevin men played trumpets in the badn.

1. _____

We saw a wite rabitt in the woods.

2. _____

Mom maed this chewy candi.

3. _____

☆ **Test-Challenge Words**

On a sheet of paper, write each challenge word as your teacher says it.

C Test-Dictation

Name _____

Listen and write the missing words.

1. _____ _____ _____ _____ stick?

2. _____ _____ _____ _____ _____ .

3. _____ _____ _____ _____ _____ _____

_____ _____ street.

D Test-Proofreading

One word in each set is misspelled. Fill in the oval by the misspelled word.

1. ◯ thik
   ◯ duck
   ◯ these

2. ◯ truck
   ◯ gras
   ◯ sick

3. ◯ uther
   ◯ those
   ◯ odd

4. ◯ guess
   ◯ thank
   ◯ funy

5. ◯ finnish
   ◯ blind
   ◯ odd

6. ◯ pond
   ◯ bak
   ◯ show

7. ◯ still
   ◯ talk
   ◯ dres

8. ◯ shoo
   ◯ shop
   ◯ should

9. ◯ find
   ◯ think
   ◯ clok

☆ **Test-Challenge Words**

On a sheet of paper, write each challenge word as your teacher says it.

Name _____

Color each picnic food on which the word is spelled incorrectly.

gess

another

theez

CHIPS

sho

podn

thoze

CHIPS

better

shood

dish

shopp

CHIPS

blidn

fidn

duk

both

sing

od

sik

☆ **Test-Challenge Words**

On a sheet of paper, write each challenge word as your teacher says it.

Name _____

At the school picnic, Rosa and other students played a tag game called "Swim, Fish, Swim!" Use types of fish as your team names for this game. Place a sticker each time you or your team spells a review word correctly.

Remember: Always be honest—even in the littlest things.

G **Test-Words**

Name _____

Write each spelling word on the line as your teacher says it.

1. _____   6. _____

2. _____   7. _____

3. _____   8. _____

4. _____   9. _____

5. _____   10. _____

H **Test-Sentences**

The two underlined words in each of the sentences are misspelled. Write the sentences on the lines below, spelling each underlined word correctly.

The litel Indin baby had brown eyes.

1. _____

At scool, the bel is very loud.

2. _____

Do you drink mutch mikl?

3. _____

☆ **Test-Challenge Words**

On a sheet of paper, write each challenge word as your teacher says it.

I **Writing Assessment**

Name _____

Write several sentences describing times you might be tempted to be dishonest. In the last sentence, write your promise to be honest all the time.

_____

_____

_____

_____

_____

_____

_____

Scripture

"Unless you are honest in small matters, you won't be in large ones."
Luke 16:10

Spelling Is Fun!

ABC's

This certificate is awarded to

_____

for practicing the following words, by doing terrific
spelling activities and playing great spelling games!

Date _____

dish	band	back	another	bell
finish	bend	bring	both	better
fish	blind	clock	other	dress
shoe	candy	duck	thank	funny
shop	end	hang	these	grass
should	find	milk	thick	guess
show	grand	sick	thin	mitten
shut	Indian	sing	think	pull
wash	kind	talk	those	rabbit
wish	pond	truck	thought	still
☆ shelf	☆ friend	☆ along	☆ brother	☆ different
☆ shoes	☆ index	☆ block	☆ father	☆ dinner
☆ short	☆ second	☆ something	☆ together	☆ letter

A Reason For SPELLING